The ESSEX Weather Book

The great floods of October/November 2000, which brought misery and heartbreak to home owners in river valleys throughout England, will be remembered as one of the three great weather events in recent history.
Essex has endured them all.
The most cataclysmic were the floods of 1953, when a storm surge whipped up the waters of the North Sea into massive tidal levels and brought tragedy to the county.
Then there was that never-to-be-forgotten night of October 16, 1987, when hurricane-force winds crippled communications and changed the face of our landscape.
Throughout history, Essex has experienced tempests and tornadoes, hailstones, and heatwaves, floods and freezes, deluges and dust devils. It remains the driest county in England yet, perversely, it floods more than most. The Met Office says it is impossible to confirm that the October/November, 2000 floods were caused by man-made global warming but they are consistent with the centre's predictions of more extreme events to come.
Our climate IS changing.

Ian Currie, Mark Davison and Bob Ogley

Froglets Publications

Brasted Chart, Westerham,
Kent TN16 1LY.
01959 562972 Fax 01959 565365

**Ian Currie, Mark Davison
and Bob Ogley**

© 1992

ISBN 1 872337 31 7

October 1992: Reprinted November 2000.

Cover illustrations

Front cover: The village of Sible
Hedingham in July 1999 where
more rain fell in one day than had
ever previously been recorded in
Essex. (Essex County Newspapers)

Back cover: Firefighters at
Gloucester Park, Basildon, in July
1994, one of the hottest Julys of
the 20th Century.
(Echo Newspapers)

This book was originated by Froglets
Publications Ltd of Brasted Chart and
printed and slot bound by
Thanet Press, Union Crescent,
Margate CT9 1NU.

Jacket design by Alison Clarke

Additional research, editing and
design by Fern Flynn

Acknowledgements

THIS is one of seven in our popular series of County Weather Books
and has been reprinted following exceptional demand from
bookshops and members of the public who were anxious to obtain
a new version that included all the most recent dramatic weather
events in Essex. The book would not have been possible without the
great co-operation from the general public, the staff of libraries and
museums, local history enthusiasts, weather buffs and the editors
and photographers of newspapers throughout the county.

In 1991 we appealed on local radio for reminiscences about
dramatic meteorological events. The response was fantastic. From
all corners of the county came anecdotes, old photographs and
newspaper cuttings. They covered remarkable blizzards, storms,
tornadoes, floods and confirmed to us that Essex is renowned for
the great variety of its weather.

We are particularly indebted to staff of local newspapers. Foremost
in helping are *The Evening Echo*, the *Essex Chronicle*, the *Essex
County Newspapers* and *Guardian Newspapers* who allowed us
access to their archives, a treasure chest of photographic memorabilia. The
Essex County Record Office, the Harlow, Chelmsford, Colchester
and Southend Museums and local libraries everywhere also helped
us to find the illustrations that truly illuminate the text.

Special thanks go to the following: H.C.Basingthwaighte of the
Burnham-on-Crouch and District Local History and Amenity
Society, Essex Water Company, Mr David Jones, Chelmsford
Museums Service, Terry Mayes and the Climatological Observers
Link, David Hart of Braintree, R.W Selfe of Thundersley, Colchester
Borough Council, Malcolm May of Chelmsford, the late T.W.Partis
of Romford, the *Essex Recorder*, the Royal Meteorological Society,
Denise Clarke of Springfield, Chelmsford, *Burnham-on-Crouch and
Dengie Hundred Advertiser*, Anglia Water, Essex Rivers Division,
Perry Sherry of Colchester, John Candlin, Sharon Buttress, Gavin
and Sue Puncher, Brian Girling, Michael Goldsmith, Mary Bryant,
Chris Hoskins, Ron Patience, Miss Dansie, Helen Cook, Richard
Shackleton, Martin Winter, Jenny Glayzer, Lynn Tait, Brian
Haggerty, Maurice Edwards, Pat Morrison, John Adams.

We referred to many books, in particular — *Journal of Meteorology*,
A Century of London Weather by J.H.Brazell, *Symon's British
Rainfall*, *The Weather of Britain* by Robin Stirling, *The Great Tide* by
Hilda Grieve, *Essex* by Norman Scarfe, *Weather Patterns in East
Anglia*, *Essex Headlines* by Stan Jarvis

Photograph credits

Echo Newspapers, Basildon: pages 51, 74, 75, 76, 77, 79,
90, 91, 113, 114, 115, 116, 119, 123, 124, 125, 127, 130,
131, 137, 138, 143, 146, 150, 158. **Topham Photographic
Agency**: 53, 54, 58, 59, 60, 64, 65, 68, 69, 70-1, 78, 80, 82,
83, 84-5, 86, 87, 88, 89, 92, 94, 95, 98, 99, 102, 104, 108,
110, 136, 141. **Essex Chronicle**: 118, 125, 129, 130, 131,
133, 134, 140, 151, 152, 153, 154, 155, 156, 157. **Essex
County Newspapers**: 66, 107, 112, 121, 122, 128, 145,
149, 159, 162 (bottom). **North London Guardian
Newspapers**: 162 (top), 163, 164. **Colchester and Essex
Museum:** 9, 14, 15, 31, 44, 51. Colchester Library: 5, 13,
14, 36, 55. **Essex Record Office**: 17, 18, 22, 23, 41, 42, 46,
56-7, 106. **Puttnams**, Walton-on-the-Naze: 7, 36, 73.
Burnham-on-Crouch Museum: 20, 23, 50, 53, 93. **Clacton
Library**: 21, 72. **Lynn Tait**, Southend: 26, 33. **G.R.
Mortimer**: 55, 100, 107, 141. **John Banks**: 120. **Romford
Observer**: 146.

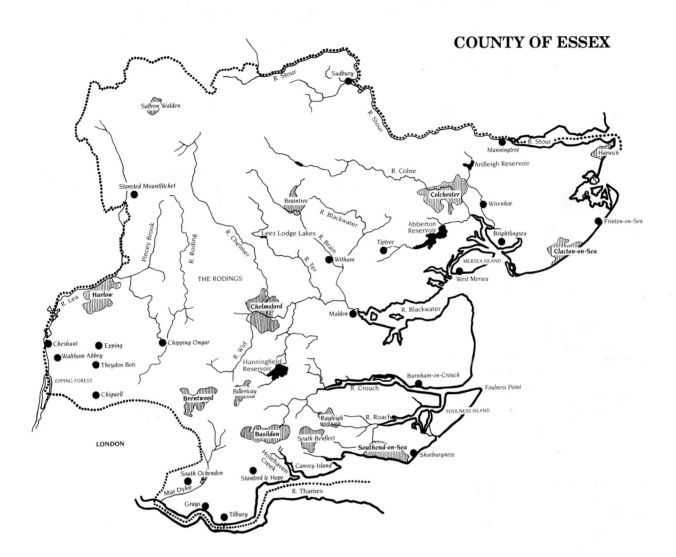

COUNTY OF ESSEX

Contents

A dry and sunny county — still haunted by the horrors of 1953

CLACTON pier has been uprooted and re-sited at Weeley roundabout, Jaywick has become an underwater playground for scuba divers and Bradwell power station is half a mile offshore. The Rowhedge postman wears an aqualung to do his daily rounds and among the best spots to launch a boat is halfway up Market Hill in Maldon.

Burnham has disappeared, what is left of Southminster is an island and one of the finest beaches in the area is barely a stone's throw from Colchester Town Hall.

This imaginative piece of reporting by the *Essex Standard* in the spring of 1989 followed a report by the environmental pressure group, Ark, on global warming. The report, said the newspaper, shows how Essex will look in the year 2050. "Atmospheric pollution has accelerated the greenhouse effect, melted the polar ice caps and raised the sea level by more than 7.5 metres (just over 24 feet)."

It suggested that most of the coastal farmland will be submerged and communities moved inland. Fishing boats will be tied up at Tolleshunt D'Arcy and Ramsey windmill converted into a lighthouse.

If the Essex coastline is inundated with flood water in 100 years' time then it is just a continuation of the greatest battle of all. The county may have stood four square against its foes from Caesar's day till now, but it has been unable to resist the greatest invader of all — the North Sea.

Whipped up by gales and vicious winds, the sea has reconstructed the coast of Essex. Cliffs have crumbled and collapsed and there have been countless landslides. Metre by metre, the sea has advanced relentlessly inland.

All this may suggest that Essex is the wettest county in England. Not true. It's the driest. Carnival committee organisers, cricketers, holidaymakers may not believe it but the average yearly rainfall in the county is a little over 20 inches. Those who live in the extreme west of the county get 25 inches; in Clacton, Southend and along the Blackwater Estuary, it is a mere 19 inches.

Essex is also included in the first sun zone in Britain, with more than 1,600 hours of annual sunshine. Southend is England's top temperature town at least once a week in the summer and the county enjoys the hottest July days of anywhere in Britain. The years 1911 and 1921 are remembered by the older generation for their long, hot, rainless summer days. The middle aged will recall the drought and heat of 1949 and 1959. Younger people can argue that 1976 was the most splendid summer of all, only to be beaten by 1989 and 1990 which dried up our vital water reserves.

Warmth breeds thunderstorms — and this means between 15 to 18 days of thunder and lightning every year in Essex. There have been numerous big inland storms but none more dramatic than that of 5th September 1958 when a hot and sticky Friday heralded an evening onslaught of three inches of rain in less than two hours.

Bitter Easterly winds can blow in unchecked from Siberia, bringing to Essex blizzards so furious at times that they remain in the memory for ever. The winter of 1962-3 was the worst since 1740. It was so severe that the sea froze and there were 68 days of lying snow in the county.

The people of Essex may have had more than their fair share of icy blasts and thundery days but the North Sea has brought, and always will bring the greatest suffering. Who can forget the floods of 1953 when 113 Essex people perished as tidal waters overtopped miles of defences and the attention of the world was focussed on places such as Canvey Island, Jaywick, Harwich, Foulness and Great Wakering?

It is impossible to exaggerate the misery and the horror of 1953 when the winds roared and the sea heaved and then came in, carrying all before it — telegraph poles and street lamps, bouncing caravans like ping pong balls, smashing sea walls to pieces and drowning people, not in their beds, but as they clambered desperately onto furniture and hung on to the tops of doors.

Engineers are trying to halt the process of erosion by building up the defences and reclaiming flooded land wherever possible, but the sea is, and always has been, the county's worst enemy. The 1953 floods led to the building of the Great Flood Barrier at Woolwich, the vast protective sea defences at Benfleet, Easthaven and Fobbing, the 280-mile long sea wall down the length of the Essex coast and additional storm-surge barriers and concrete parapets wherever there was doubt.

Despite the seemingly indestructable nature of these costly defences, the sea continues to bite away at Essex every year.

It is a constant reminder of the terror endured by the county in 1953 — a terror that exceeds anything that Essex, or Britain, has ever experienced.

Wind against the tide. Tilbury Fort in 1849

Those in peril on the North Sea

AS fishermen and sailors have known for centuries and oilmen have discovered more recently, the North Sea is a moody, challenging, perilous stretch of water and particularly wild and unpredictable during the winter months. The Essex coast has proved a watery graveyard for thousands of ships. From the dangerous maze of sandbanks at the mouth of the Thames, the treacherous Gunfleet sands off Clacton where so many have come to grief to the storm-battered seas off Harwich, many fine ships have foundered — victims of war, fire, questionable seamanship but, most of all, the fury of the North Sea.

In September 1671, 76 ships foundered in a storm and there was so much wreckage floating about that masters had to be particularly cautious. On another wild night in 1692, no less than 200 ships and more than 1,000 men went down.

The dreaded Gunfleet has claimed many lives, although in 1839, 14 ships were blown onto the sands and not one life was lost. Another spectacular incident with a happy ending occurred on 17th February, 1843 when a terrible gale blew the brig *Traveller* on the the Gunfleet. The crew lashed themselves to the rigging and went through the night feeling the ship break up under their feet.

They were seen, being washed and battered, by the crew of two smacks from Colchester who, despite the violence of the sea, effected a most dramatic rescue.

Not so lucky were the crew and passengers of a German ship the *Deutschland*, sailing from Bremen to New York with passengers looking forward to a new life in America. Fifty of them didn't make it. On Saturday 4th December, 1875 the ship ran into dense fog which was cleared by an easterly gale with driving snow. She was driven aground on the Kentish Knock, another long sandbank, off Harwich. 155 were rescued but the rest perished in the freezing seas. It was this most appalling tragedy which led to the stationing of a lifeboat in Harwich in 1876.

The list of ships lost in stormy weathers off the Essex Coast is a very long one, from wooden sailing ships, to steam ships and motor vessels and, more recently, to steel-strong, self propelled ships better able to withstand the hammer blows of wind and wave. Lifeboats from Harwich to Southend have put to sea in the most dreadful weather saving, over the years, thousands of lives and providing some of the most heroic and spectacular rescues on record. Many brave lifeboatmen have themselves become victims of the gales.

At war with the waves

ESSEX is like a walled fortress. More than 300 miles of defences form a massive barrier against the thrusting tides of the North Sea. They run in an almost unbroken sequence from Judas Gap at the head of the Stour, across muddy saltings, round creeks and quays and seaside towns, over flat marshland to the Thames Dockland, once wharfs and warehouses, now commerce and commuters.

Several times a year monstrous storm-driven waves crash against the barriers. Every now and again they are breached and part of Essex is inundated. Driven by the winds, the tides frequently probe into the heart of the county via the rivers, creeks and estuaries, which are like arms of the sea.

The defences are the result of 2,000 years' work. Each generation from Roman times has experienced at least one storm "of a ferocity not remembered by the oldest inhabitant". Waves, rising to a great height have caused a disaster "which will remain in the recollection of those who experienced them to their dying day."

Many townships and villages have disappeared into the waves for much of Essex is below the high water mark and, for centuries, communities have lived with the fear of extinction. Much of Old Walton now lies on the sea bed, including a parish church dating back to the thirteenth century. A forest of yews exists under the sea between Purfleet and Grays. Roman remains have been found below the high water mark at Clacton. The fort of Othona at Bradwell-on-Sea is lost under saltings and at West Tilbury a Romano-British hut circle is buried on the Thames foreshore.

The problem lies with the tides and their effects which, in Essex, are unpredictable. In places they have silted up creeks while devouring land at will. But though the tides may nibble and encroach twice a day, the flooding and possible destruction of a piece of coastline have been caused by the really tremendous storms, the exceptional events that have been so well documented over the centuries.

Mediaeval chroniclers regarded the great Essex storms and tides as phenomena but also as judgements on the wickedness of men and as portents of things to come. The Anglo-Saxon Chronicle recorded in 1099: "This year also, on the festival of St Martin, the sea sprung up to such a height, and did so much harm, as no man remembered that it ever did before. And this was the first day of the new moon."

In November 1236, Matthew Paris, describing one combination of wind and sea wrote: "Suddenly a most mightie wind resounded, with great and unusual sea and river floods together which deprived all ports of ships, tearing away their anchors, drowned a multitude of men, destroyed flocks of sheep and herds of cattle, plucked out trees by the roots, overturned dwellings and dispersed beaches. And the ocean rose flowing with increase for two days and one night...then there were seen the unburied bodies of the drowned lying in sea caves by the sea shore."

The period from the 11th to the 15th century saw a series of great tidal floods which struck like the blows of a battering ram. In 1320, the banks of the Thames were in a complete state of collapse. In 1326 breaching was incessant between Stratford and Tilbury and, in 1392 through inroads of the sea onto land belonging to St Osyth Abbey, "the revenues of the monks were seriously diminished."

In 1570 there was a "greate storm" in which livestock losses all along the east coast were catastrophic. The sea wall also collapsed in places. The Elizabethan chronicler, Hollinshed recalled how, in one community, a bridge was shattered, more than 2,000 head of livestock drowned, 480 acres of land, sown with corn, swamped and 13 houses completely ruined.

It was the same sad story in the 17th and 18th centuries. Great tides still swept out of the north, gaining height and momentum on their way south. In 1703 and 1736 there were severe surges. That of February 1736 swamped the coastal lands from Lincolnshire to Kent, drowning thousands of cattle along with their owners who were trying to save them. Foulness was entirely under water. "Not a hoof was saved thereon, and the Inhabitants were taken from the upper Part of their Houses into Boats."

By now the problem of sea defence in Essex was receiving much attention. Key areas listed as particularly vulnerable included Jaywick, the Dengie Peninsula, Canvey Island and Thameside. The cost was valued at thousands of pounds and it mounted with the increasing height of the walls.

By the 18th century it was not only the coastal farmers who were anxious for the Essex coast to be securely defended from the ravages of the sea. Industry was expanding particularly along the Thames estuary, seaside towns were springing up and an expanding population was making it clear that continued salt-water flooding of so much productive land could not be tolerated.

The battle continued.

Warships blown to Sweden

26th November, 1703

ARGUABLY the most powerful storm ever to have visited our shores swept across southern England on the night of 26th November, 1703. The writer, Daniel Defoe of *Robinson Crusoe* fame, and a keen weather watcher experienced the sheer terror of the storm in London and published a documentary account of it.

From his description and the many reports sent to him, including one from the Reverend Derham of Upminster, it was a catastrophic tempest followed by a "prodigious tide". The death toll amounted to 8,000 on land and at sea with 400 windmills and 800 houses demolished and countless trees blown down.

Ships at anchor on the Thames were blown from their moorings and piled together between Bell Wharf and Limehouse in a manner described as "impossible and incredible. Nobody," he said, "could believe the hundreth part they saw."

The Reverend Derham had devised his own measurement of storm strength. In 1693 he gave one storm a reading of 10 and another in 1701 of nine, whereas he assigned the figure of 15 to that of 1703. Offshore at Harwich, Admiral Cloudesley Shovell's flagship together with a large fleet of warships, just back from a summer campaign in the Mediterranean, had to raise anchor and let the wind take them. Some of the fleet blew to Holland, others to Sweden. Elsewhere many ships were sunk.

One of the most dramatic incidents was the loss of the Eddystone Lighthouse and its builder, Winstanley, who was on the reef checking further improvements and caught the full force of the storm. There was no trace of him, his workmen, the keepers or the lighthouse. Ironically, his own house in Essex was also destroyed.

This ancient sketch is of the thirteenth century Walton Church which has been swallowed up by the sea and is no longer visible. It shows the church in 1777 in a bad state of repair with the tower collapsed. In spite of these conditions and the constant threat from the encroaching sea, services were held right up to 1789 when the roof fell in during a storm. By then the church was standing right at the water's edge, and parish business, plus an occasional wedding was carried out in the porch until finally, in 1798, the sea completely overwhelmed it during another storm. At very low tides the remains of the foundations were still seen this century, several times during the 1920's, and even as recently as 1950.

CHAPTER ONE   1800 - 1889

Last Frost Fair on the Thames

1808: At Plaistow, a reading of 96F (36C) was recorded on Wednesday 13th July by Luke Howard, who was instrumental in devising a cloud classification, now used throughout the world.

1814: In an exceptionally harsh winter, hundreds of starved rooks were removed from woodland at Sheepcotes, Little Waltham. The severe cold also took toll on rabbits and hares and trees were denuded of bark to the height at which animals could graze. Average temperatures for January were below 27F (-3C) This month saw the last great Frost Fair on the Thames in London.

1821: Air pressure fell to 28.05 inches of mercury (950 millibars) on Christmas Day, a value not matched until 25th February, 1989.

1829: The weather was so excessively raw on 9th October that "it could scarce be matched even in the middle of winter". Snow fell unmixed with rain and lay several inches deep on the ground.

1836: A wet October culminated in a heavy snowfall on the 29th which lay for several days. A temperature reading of 24F (-4C) was recorded at Southchurch, extremely low for so early in the winter. The total rainfall for the autumn amounted to 11.6 inches, or half the yearly average.

1838: On 20th January, metropolitan Essex recorded temperatures of -4F (-20C) — then one of the lowest for 200 years. To cheer themselves up on 18th January, the men of Gosfield and Halstead scraped the hoar frost off their cricket bats and played a game on Gosfield Lakes. All the players wore skates.

1841: After a sharp frost in January, a heavy snowfall blanketed the streets of Colchester. As the ice and snows thawed, the River Colne overflowed its banks.

1846: The warmest June on record with 16 days above 80F (27C) in East London.

1854: A prodigious snowfall occurred on Wednesday 4th January after a spell of intense cold. Chelmsford was like a besieged town with drifts seven feet deep at Widford. On the Eastern Union line all services were suspended from Colchester through to Norwich. The roads were no better. At Little Dunmow Street, the way was blocked by drifts nine feet deep and the mail cart became stuck fast. The sharpness of the frost was illustrated by a curious incident. A child on Halstead town bridge happened by chance to put his tongue briefly on the iron railing. To his astonishment he was completely frozen to it. Hot water was procured and the little prisoner released.

1855: Ice hindered navigation on the Thames in February and thousands of dockers were out of work. Quantities of ice were seen drifting out to sea.

1860: Diarist Ellen Buxton, then aged 12, wrote "Ever since the middle of December there has been skating and we have been nearly every day to Wanstead pond". On Christmas Day, the temperature fell to 8F (-14C), the coldest reading since February 1845.

1861: A cold January, an oppressively hot spell in August and an October in which the temperature reached 76F (25C).

1879: A very cold year. At Braintree it was described as 'the most disastrous ever remembered' for agricultural farmers and, at Dunmow, for the "ruination of hay, corn, roots and fruit".

1881: After the rigours of an icy winter the mercury soared to heatwave values on 18th July, reaching 90F (32C) at Southend.

1884: Leyton Observatory reported a remarkably dry year in which many ponds became completely devoid of water and the bogs in Epping Forest passable throughout the summer and autumn. At Dunmow some wells became dry " a circumstance not remembered by the oldest inhabitant".

1887: During a severe spell of icy weather, snow was cleared from the streets of Colchester under the superintendence of the borough surveyor. More than 200 men were employed in removing the snow and 15 carts were used.

*This old print of Southend was published in 1824, just a few years after Jane Austen's Mrs John Knightly in **Emma** said: "We all had our health perfectly there; never found the least inconvenience from the mud." This handsome town and fashionable watering place, on the north bank of London's river, was developing into a flourishing holiday resort. Local businessmen competed for their share in the "sunshine market," together with outside investors who were building hotels, theatres and a wooden pier which advanced elegantly seawards in front of The Marine Library. The resort was actually established at the south end of the village of Prittlewell and grew rapidly after the railway was opened in 1856.*

Haymaking at Lexden, Colchester in June 1858, one of the hottest Junes ever known. In the 19th century, Lexden was a fashionable garden village surrounded by evergreen trees. This is one of the earliest photographs taken in the Colchester area.

Worst blizzard ever known

January 1881

THIS was the blizzard of the century. It began on 18th January, 1881 and raged for more than 24 hours, forcing blinding snow into every crack and crevice. The snow was so deep that trains, horses, carts and even houses were completely buried. Towns and villages were unrecognisable under the thick, white carpet and many people died at sea and on land.

On Wednesday 19th January, the people of Essex woke up to the magnitude of the disaster. East coast lifeboats had capsized with many lives lost, all communication across land had been severed and people had died from frostbite and exposure.

The deafening, easterly wind whipped up the Thames and North Sea into a frenzy and giant waves crashed onto the coastline, wrecking promenades and flooding coastal homes. Fifty barges in the Thames between East Ham and Tilbury were sunk and one man was found frozen to death on another barge. Portions of Southend pier were carried away and, inland, the snow formed drifts 17 feet deep at Norton Heath and seven feet at Barking, where ice floes six inches thick massed on the Thames.

The worst tragedies were at sea where valiant attempts were made in atrocious conditions to rescue crews from stricken crafts. On land, the blizzard was remorseless and some who ventured outside were found, next day, entombed in snowdrifts.

Near Thorp le Soken, a gardener was hit by a falling chimney. A groom, Abraham Johnson of Beaumont Hall set out to look for a doctor to attend to the man but lost his way and was found dead in a field the next day. In Romford, a man using a hoe to probe the drifts touched upon the body of a young woman. She had set out from Whalebone Lane to visit her sick husband in the Romford Union Workhouse Infirmary. The wild weather in Felsted claimed the life of labourer, Arthur Shuttlewood who, in the teeth of the blizzard, was struck by a train.

Many trains came to grief. One left Southend at 2.45 pm, scheduled to reach London two hours later. At Thames Haven it came to a halt in six feet of snow and the passengers waited two hours to be rescued. They were eventually lifted out, led through a cutting in the snow and then across fields to an inn. By daylight on Wednesday, the train was completely buried and not even the funnel of the engine could be seen. One hundred men were engaged in digging a passage along the Maldon line. It was almost 24 hours before the first train could get through to Witham.

The Clacton lifeboat, *Albert Edward,* went to the aid of a stricken Norwegian boat which had almost capsized on the Maplin Sands. The crew of seven had spent 18 hours on a sinking ship and were discovered knee deep in the icy water. The Essex Chronicle noted: "The wretched men were landed at the pier at 3.40 on Thursday morning, the plucky lifeboat crew giving three hearty cheers as they brought them ashore. Even the lifeboatmen felt the cold considerably, some of their hands being much swollen yet not a complaint was heard; their only thought seemed to be of those they had saved from a watery grave."

Two days later the Clacton lifeboatmen, joined by the crew of the Harwich and Lowestoft lifeboat, rescued 15 men from a vessel at Sunk Sand. Another eight were feared drowned, having spent three freezing days and nights on the rigging.

In another life-saving mission, the Harwich lifeboat, *Springwell* could not be launched from her usual site because of the tremendous tide. She was taken to the Continental Pier and lifted into the sea on a crane. The crowd "cheered lustily" but, as the lifeboat set off into the south easterly winds, she was toppled by a cruel gust. The lifeboat righted herself but William Wink, aged 55, one of the crew, drowned. The boat drifted with the flood tide at a rapid rate towards Mistley, near Manningtree. On this day the shores around Harwich and Dovercourt were littered with smashed smacks and schooners. At least two people fell overboard and died.

Inland, it was a sea of snow which caused so much distress. In Harlow, eight carts were completely buried and at Netteswell Cross near Burnt Mill Station, a pub was buried by snow up to the roof. It was up to the hedgetops in the Ongar Road at Brentwood and a hay cart was blown over.

Green spectacles, which protected eyes from the dazzling snow, were in demand at Chelmsford but otherwise trade in the town was virtually suspended. The *Chronicle* wrote: "Driving and walking were next to impossible. Such few men and animals that were abroad only maintained their equilibrium with difficulty and they looked like so many perambulating masses of snow".

At Leigh-on-Sea, homes were swamped and dozens of boats wrecked. "They were tossed out of the sea like cockle shells", said the *Chronicle*, "and residents were forced to move to the top floors of their flooded homes". At Southend, a barge smashed into the pier and chiselled out a 25-yard gap, causing all traffic on the pier to cease.

The 1881 blizzard had earned a place in folklore.

The Half Moon Inn at the junction of London Road and the High Street, Chelmsford after the great snow storm of 18th January, 1881.

The Great English Earthquake

22nd April, 1884

IN the rural farming district of north-east Essex, the morning of 22nd April, 1884 dawned fine and clear and only the occasional cloud disturbed a faultless sky. Wisps of smoke from chimney pots hung in long trails against the blue backdrop. The thermometer was rising, the barometer was high. It was a perfect spring morning.

At 9.18 am there was a loud rumbling noise from the earth that built up to a tremendous intensity. The ground oscillated, buildings and chimneys swayed, chimney stacks tumbled over, houses and cottages shook and crashed open, slates cascaded down roofs into the streets below, walls burst outwards, masonry fell and explosions of smoke and debris rose into the air. Doors opened and shut, bells rang and the whole countryside rose up and down like waves in a storm-tossed sea.

As terrified people stumbled from their homes they were thrown to the ground. Some were screaming, some were sick and many tried desperately to stay on their feet. Suddenly, the wave motion slowed down and stopped. Dust was still rising and the occasional sickening crack of another doomed building filled the air.

The unthinkable had happened. In less than a minute Britain had experienced an earthquake (6.9 on the Richter scale) and Essex was left with scars which she bears to this day.

The Great British Earthquake, as it was to become known, was centred on the small agricultural communities south-east of Colchester. From here it fanned out rapidly right across England, disturbing an area of more than 53,000 square miles. It was registered as far away as Somerset to the west and Cheshire to the north. Shock waves travelled to Belgium and France.

The actual impact was felt across a radius of 150 miles and it shattered 1,200 buildings — shops, homes, schools, churches, factories and workshops. In the village of Wivenhoe the entire population was made homeless.

The *Essex Standard* said that not within living memory had Colchester been thrown into such a state of excitement, consternation and panic as it was soon after 9 o'clock on Tuesday morning.

"Everything was peaceful and quiet early in the morning, no fresh atmospherical change from the last few days with the exception of a slight elevation of temperature, being experienced to indicate in any way the approach of a visitation of this nature, from which England happily has been very free, and has had little or no cause to anticipate anything of the kind either in years gone by or at this more immediate period.

"The awful event came without the slightest warning and lasted from five to ten seconds but in that short period of time, an amount of damage was done to property which it will take weeks to set right, and in some cases destruction is irreparable.

"From one end of the town to the other the ground was convulsed, and if a spectator could have taken a bird's eye view of the Borough, the effect would have been much the same as a sea wave, the ground upheaving and lowering by means of that gigantic power pent up beneath the earth's crust. The general impression appears to be that the ground and the houses with it was lifted up, shaken two or three times in a manner that made the stoutest heart quake, and the bravest to cow with fear, and then subside, disappearing with a kind of final shake or jerk, and then it was all over."

Abberton, south of Colchester, was just above the epicentre and every house in the village was damaged. The chimney stack toppled through the roof of the Lion Inn, and amazingly only one glass in the bar was shattered. Churches in the three villages of Breton, Marney and De-La-Haye were damaged and, at Langenhoe, the church was so badly mutilated that it could not be used again and was never rebuilt. Langenhoe Hall had most of its roof shaken off.

At Peldon, the battlements of the church tower fell through the roof of the nave and its walls were cracked and shifted out of position. The church tower at Wivenhoe developed a crack half its height from the top and the shock caused the turrets to break away completely.

It was at Wivenhoe where the worst destruction occurred. Ferrymen, fishermen and wealthy yacht owners heard the booming sound below ground and then watched giant waves toss their boats in the air. An old ferryman, Jones, had just landed on the hard when the earthquake struck. He saw boats roll like "floating corks" and felt the whole quay "on the move as if going right down".

"It seemed just like three seas", he said, "And the waves on the river became a great wave on the land which disappeared over the hill who knows where...."

At The Anchor in Wivenhoe, landlady Mrs Dick Ham was flung back against the counter as the wave-like motion lifted the floor of the bar upwards. Glasses tumbled all around her, beer casks rolled

Langenhoe Church was so badly mutilated that it could not be used again

over and plaster fell from the ceiling. Mrs Ham was knocked out by something which struck her from behind. As she lay unconscious, beams twisted and split and she was covered by the debris. She was pulled clear by her husband who was outside at the time and had managed to evade the falling chimney pot from the inn.

At the National School in Wivenhoe High Street, 70 children had just finished assembly when the rumbling began. Walls cracked and floors heaved and the children were thrown among the enveloping dust and debris. Headmaster, Mr Collins, managed to prevent a panic-stricken riot and herded them out into the playground, a number suffering from bruises.

All around the village there was confusion and fear. Houses and cottages, packed tightly together, presented "very woeful and dilapidated aspects". Some people in the streets were only half-dressed and others were covered in blood from cuts and scratches.

In Colchester, the 9.20 am express train to London was at the main downline platform when the station master, Mr Blatch, heard the sound of distant thunder. "The platform beneath my feet began to heave. I felt dizzy in the head and fell against the wall of the platform".

Mr Blatch watched the engine and carriages of the train rise and fall, the carriages banging against each other. Doors sprang open and the engine driver was thrown out of his cab onto the platform. As steam escaped from the engine, passengers poured from compartments with cut arms and faces.

The massive spire of the Lion Walk Congregational Church was shaken down and part of it plunged into the graveyard, demolishing tombstones and, in the High Street, there was the scene of unprecented panic as people were bowled over and horses shied and ran amok.

Mersea Island, the beauty spot just off the Essex coast, flanked by the estuaries of the Colne and Blackwater, experienced the most terrifying effects, for on the higher hinterland, the ground groaned and moved under the stresses of the earthquake — then suddenly split and opened up. One eye witness described it as "the very jaws of hell".

In Langenhoe, the devastation was complete. The *Essex Standard* wrote: "The scene in this parish of 230 souls is spoken of by eye witnesses as most painful in the extreme - women and children rushed out of their houses in the greatest terror, many of them shrieking in the roads, whole men were also startled. How many of the poor people whose houses have thus been wrecked, are to find shelter for themselves and their families for some little time, is more than we can say."

Peter Haining in his book *The Great British Earthquake* describes it as one of the forgotten chapters of British history, scarcely known out-

A cottage at Peldon which presented a"very woeful aspect".

side the environs of Colchester. "The event was a stunning blow to Victorian England, the heart of the great British Empire. It seemed to undermine the very stability of the Nation — and consequently its extent and damage were played down by the authorities and the national press".

That the devastation should have fallen upon Essex was also a cruel blow for at the time the county was suffering from an agricultural depression, probably more severely than any other part of England.

The Earthquake of 1884 was the most destructive known in the country. It came like a crack of doom and had a remarkable effect by filling churches with worshippers who feared that more such disturbances would follow. On that bright spring morning, the county of Essex, and particularly the area around Colchester, took a place in history as the site of the greatest earthquake that Britain had ever experienced.

The Bell Inn at Old Heath, a casualty of the earthquake. It was to survive until 1936 when it was demolished.

THE GRAPHIC

AN ILLUSTRATED WEEKLY NEWSPAPER

No. 753—Vol. XXIX.
Registered as a Newspaper

SATURDAY, MAY 3, 1884

WITH EXTRA
SUPPLEMENT

PRICE SIXPENCE
By Post Sixpence Halfpenny

EXTERIOR OF LANGENHOE CHURCH

INTERIOR OF LANGENHOE CHURCH

CONGREGATIONAL CHURCH, LION WALK, COLCHESTER
(The dotted portion of the Steeple was shaken down)

IN THE HYTHE, COLCHESTER: THE RUSH FOR THE GASWORKS

PELDON CHURCH

ROSE INN, PELDON

ON THE QUAY, WIVENHOE

COTTAGE AT ABBERTON

THE RECENT DISASTROUS EARTHQUAKE IN EAST ESSEX

The bridge was swept away

July - August, 1888

IT was dubbed by many at the time as 'The year without a summer'. Cricket was played but conditions were so cold, wet and sunless that the season dragged on into the autumn. On 11th July, 1888 snow fell in Romford, Sawbridgeworth and Stock. At Earls Colne, according to one observer, partridges perished in the cold. There were frequent thunderstorms — two within a week at Great Leighs, where lightning twice struck the same tree. In these cold, damp conditions mushrooms flourished and, at Galleywood, one measured two feet across.

The end of July saw an intensification of the severe weather. Thunderstorms and torrential rain brought 4.1 inches (105 mm) in five days at Chelmsford and nearly four inches in just two days at Ilford. The saturated fields could not absorb the water. Rain fell unceasingly all day on Wednesday 1st August. Thunder filled the air. Lightning struck several houses including that of Mr Durrant, the draper of Chelmsford High Street. It showered the deserted rain-swept yard below with bricks and mortar.

During the early hours of this day, residents of Chelmsford were aroused by floodwaters gushing into their homes and they gathered in huddled misery in upper rooms. Meanwhile, the sight at dawn of the swollen, muddy yellow water surging past the London Road bridge with irresistable force was awe-inspiring. A willow tree was torn up and, still vertical, hurled against the bridge. A combination of the furious assault by millions of gallons of turbulent floodwaters and the enhanced scouring effect on a stone buttress, caused by the misplaced tree, was too much for the bridge. The structure was quickly evacuated and, with a loud crash, the whole mass of iron and roadway fell bodily into the stream leaving the mass of spectators separated by a churning gulf of foaming waters. It was just before eight o'clock.

There was another major occurrence in the brickfields of Mr James Brown at New Writtle Street, where fire in two of the kilns destroyed 30,000 bricks. Thousands of moulded unburnt bricks in sheds were submerged under several feet of water and they were reduced to a large mass of boggy clay. Eight men had to be rescued by boat from the Water Mill near Widford Bridge. The men had tried, unsuccessfully, to stop hay floating downstream and becoming entangled in the works of the mill. As the waters rose they were forced to spend an uncomfortable night, perched high on the beams.

Viewed from a dry vantage point on top of St Mary's Church tower a scene, which few could imagine, stretched in the direction of Writtle and Widford. Meadow after meadow was a sheet of water, while nearer at hand gardens were swamped and destroyed and basements filled almost to their ceilings. Imprisoned residents of The Friars and Barrack Square hauled up their food by ropes. The pressure of the water was so great that a front door burst in and the muddy torrent rose above the mantel piece. One man waded through the flood holding his clothes above his head shouting: "Does anybody have a house to let as I want to get dressed?"

The wall of the British School was swept away and the expensive oak herringbone floor ruined. There were those who sought to gain from the calamity, such as the owners of traps who were crying — "through the sea for tuppence, sir". Others waded waist deep past floating barrels, boxes and staves carrying people pick-a-back.

At Romford an immense amount of property was destroyed, the River Rom becoming a huge conduit of flood water, trapping innumerable families in their upstairs rooms as it burst its banks. The Ind Coope Brewery was inundated and up to 30,000 empty casks were washed away in a mad voyage downstream. Three or four hundred kilderkilns of unbunged ale were also lost and the brewery horses were up to their chests in water before they were rescued from the stables.

At one point the water reached an overwhelming eight feet, almost level with the bedroom window sills at the Coach and Horses Inn. Big losses were sustained at the Golden Lion Hotel and The Fancy Repository lost vast quantities of merchandise. The prodigious force of the flood was best illustrated by the bizarre incident at the cottage of a Mrs Bird, where flooring was thrown up with such violence that a flower vase standing on a table in the centre of the room was embedded in the ceiling above and remained for all to see.

Many animals were drowned, one man losing 17 sheep and another, 40 head of poultry. At Oldchurch, hundreds of casks from the brewery were rescued, many men assisting in the task. One man slipped and fell and was carried away by the current under the bridge. He managed to grasp an overhanging branch and clung on until he was rescued. Later in the day, another drama was to unfold at the same spot. A man and a boy fell into the flood while trapping casks of beer and were pulled out with the aid of ropes thrown to them.

The road outside the Windmill Inn, Chelmsford on 1st August, 1888.

Beyond Romford, rail traffic was interrupted when hundreds of tons of earth slipped onto the track. At Ilford, the line was submerged for a mile or so. An observer at Wethersfield in the north of the county wrote: "The storm on Monday was of a most extraordinary character, the rain falling in sullen floods. It seemed as if the very windows of heaven were opened".

An analysis of the rainfall figures reveal why there was so much devastation. At Epping, July and August brought 11.7 inches (299 mm) of rain, about 40 per cent of the annual rainfall. In Romford, about one sixth of an average year's rain fell on 1st August.

The disappearing iron bridge attracted many spectators on that historic day in 1888.

Chelmsford's streets were turned to rivers in the deluge of 1st August, 1888

CHAPTER TWO   1890 - 1899

Skaters enjoy a decade of ice

1890:   The Chelmsford Hunt Steeplechase was postponed three times at Galleywood due to frost and snow, and then abandoned.   This sudden plunge to freezing weather took place in the last week of November and continued into December, when the cold intensified to such a degree that the month became the coldest ever recorded. Temperatures plunged to 0F (-18C) in Chelmsford, rivers and pipes were frozen, and delivered milk contained lumps of ice. In South Fambridge, a man was found frozen to death.

1891:   Early January brought ideal skating conditions on the river between Chelmsford and Maldon attracting, on one day, more than 2,000 people. A race between two men took place on the 13-mile stretch from Maldon to Springfield and a man bicycled the distance without mishap.

At Felbridge on the Blackwater, the captains of ice-bound vessels roasted a joint of meat on the ice and served hot teas at 1d a cup.

A fierce snowstorm on 9th March led to fearful conditions at sea. There were several wrecks on the Gunfleet Sands and the Black Knolls. The captain of one schooner was drowned and another crew member, who lashed himself to the top mast, succumbed to exposure.

Bitterly cold winds led to a cheerless Whitsun with top coats and fires being the order of the day. A snowstorm at Margaretting and Ingatestone on Saturday 16th May was followed by severe frost and ice. Holiday traffic on the Great Eastern Railway amounted to 35,000 passengers, compared to 135,000 the previous year.

1892: Another cold year. On Tuesday 28th June, thunder 'resembling the discharge of a thousand pieces of heavy artillery', passed across Essex. Houses at Moors Hall, Little Bardfield, North Ockendon and Tendring were struck by lightning and several barns, shelters and sheds burnt to the ground. The sails at Great Holland Mill were shattered and animals struck down. At Halstead, an ear-splitting peal of thunder so startled an old man that he died of a heart attack and an eight-year-old Purfleet girl terrified of the wild and stormy night, fell ill and also died.

1893: A bitterly cold start to the year with temperatures not rising above 23F (-5C). An ice carnival with skaters in fancy dress was held on The Cutting at added to the brilliancy of the scene.

The spring was remarkable for its lack of rain. Britain's longest run of rainless days was recorded at Mile End with 73 days between 4th March to 15th May. A partial drought of 128 days was attained at North Ockendon (average rainfall less than 0.01 inches per day). No grass grew, the crops perished, birds struggled to survive and the ground cracked on hard clay soils.

1894: An icy start to the year with temperatures on Friday 5th January falling close to 0F(-18C) at Chelmsford. Pipes froze and standpipes were provided, attracting a throng of anxious people clutching their pails. Ice piled on the shore at Walton-on-the-Naze and Brightingsea, frozen surf festooned promenade railings and, of course, skaters were in their element. Thousands visited Dagenham Lake, where the metropolitan branch of the National Skating Association held a quarter-mile race for amateurs.   (continued)

The coldest December on record was in 1890

Many of England's well-known cold spells set in after Christmas but in 1890, Jack Frost took a firm grip on 25th November and refused to let go for 59 days. The Thames was blocked with ice in places but it was the harmful effect on bird life which worried the *Essex Naturalist*.

Sparrows and starlings unreservedly fed on the scraps thrown out by kindly people but thrushes, blackbirds and finches missed out on the bounty and many were found dead. Fish also suffered. Some were found gasping for air through holes in the ice on ponds still shallow from an autumn drought.

In the London area, there were 27 days when the temperature remained at or below freezing during the daytime. It was the most prolonged December frost of the century in parts of Essex.

It was little wonder that ice formed on the River Can at Chelmsford and skaters came out in force. On Saturday 13th December, hundreds of candles were lit around obstacles on the ice to divert skaters away from danger. "It was a novel spectacle", said the *Essex Chronicle*.

Skating on the Blackwater in Maldon in January 1892. This was one of many cold winters in the last decade of the nineteenth century.

Rector appeals for help

(1890 - 1899 continued)

1894: A violent thunderstorm shook south-east Essex in the early hours of 24th September. The rector of Woodham Walter, near Maldon made this plea for help in the *Essex Chronicle*: "I appeal on behalf of the inhabitants whose homes were wrecked and who lost furniture by the great and sudden flood which swept through our village. Many of the cottages are in ruins, the village postmistress has lost her all, three cottages are hopelessly wrecked. Subscriptions will be thankfully received." At nearby Danbury, two inches (50 mm) of rain fell.

1895: Another winter of arctic severity, especially in February when the temperature fell to below 0F (-18C). It was the coldest February of the 19th century. All non-tidal rivers were covered with thick ribbed ice and roads were as hard as iron. Migration and death cleared the county of birds to an unprecedented extent. All kinds of vegetation suffered and nurserymen and market gardeners were particularly hard hit.

In these conditions on a thickly-iced lake at Gate House, Ingatestone, Mr Philip Sherrin's cricket team played an eleven arranged by Mr Joseph Coverdale. Although the date was Saturday 2nd February, many of the players were in regular July form. The fielding was generally smart, but frequent tumbles and collisions "afforded plenty of amusement for the large company who gathered to witness the match".

Snowstorms, thunderstorms and floods swept through Essex in 1894. Warmer weather did arrive in the summer and those who arrived at Clacton for their summer holiday had a pleasant surprise. The pier had been extended and many more bathing huts provided, especially for the ladies.

When harvesting began in June

(1890 - 1899 continued)

1896: What was described as a "perfect hurricane" blew in at 3 pm on Wednesday 15th January. There was thunder, lightning and great gusts which caused people on the streets to fall over. At Maldon, a chimney stack fell through the roof of a house in the Market Hall "doing great mischief".

The first crop of the year, a field of barley, was cut on 24th June at West Tilbury. It was one of the earliest dates ever known for the start of harvesting.

1897: Severe hailstorms on 24th June ruined crops, smashed glass, injured people caught out in the open and caused great damage to the decorations set out for Queen Victoria's Diamond Jubilee. The destruction was so great around Ingatestone that it was dubbed "black Tuesday."

1898: The second half of August and all of September was dry and hot. The warmest day of the year occurred as late as 8th September when the temperature was 90F (32C) in Metropolitan Essex. Grass burnt, wells ran dry and springs diminished. A spell of rain in October led to the fastest growth of grass ever for this month, according to one observer in Upminster.

1899: Another dry year. At Bocking it was the seventh in a row. The lack of rain caused great hardship in Billericay and a report from Havering said that ordinary wells, dry in 1898, failed to recover.

There was a heavy fall of rain on 23rd July when two inches (50mm) fell in the space of a few hours. The Braintree district was badly affected and crops were found floating in pools of water. In Panfield Road, Braintree, a house was struck by lightning and "great oak beams were split up like so much matchwood. A room where a Miss Horniblow was sleeping bore the brunt of this fiery visitation".

Ha'penny meals for the hungry

February 1895

AN incredible iron frost gripped Essex in February 1895 and led to so much hardship and distress that hundreds of men were put out of work and soup kitchens set up to alleviate the problems of the "poor and perishing".

January 1895 had been an exceptionally cold month but temperatures recovered to about 50F (10C) by the 20th. However, the bitterly cold weather from the continent returned with a vengeance.

On 7th February, Chelmsford Town Council agreed that a half-penny be charged for a quart of soup and a slice of bread. The Bishop of Colchester sent £5 to the cause and urged people to donate coal to the poor.

Hundreds of quarts of welcome broth and suet dumplings were served to those who braved the queues in Chelmsford's freezing weather. One man could not wait. He broke into St. James' parish church at Greenstead Green, stole a loaf of bread and ate it in the pews.

In Maldon, a feast at St Mary's Mission Hall was arranged for the impoverished; this included a whole chicken donated by the City Stores. The next day, 160 children enjoyed the remains of the supper and, on another night, tramps were entertained to a soup supper.

The wildlife also suffered. At Heybridge, large flocks of seagulls were fed by the "kindly inhabitants of Well Terrace" while, at Springfield, several hundred crop-pecking pigeons were shot.

On 11th February, Britain's coldest ever temperature was attained, -17F (-27.2C), at Braemar in Scotland*. On this day in Essex a man died from the cold, at Hornchurch and another found unconscious near Dunmow Town Hall.

Graceful skating at Wanstead in the big freeze of 1895. Away from these lighter momemts, there was severe hardship.

He was removed to the Union House Infirmary.

On the Thames, ships were welded in by the ice and a barge mate froze to death. On Saturday 9th February, a deserted yacht was found at Dovercourt. It was towed to harbour but floating ice cut through the timbers and it sank.

It was so cold at Saffron Walden that a lady put a hot brick in her bed to warm the sheets. It worked — the bedclothes caught fire and Mrs Gilbey, in a semi-conscious state, was rescued by a neighbour.

Curling became fashionable, a moonlit tobogganing festival was held at Saffron Walden and an ice carnival was held near Dunmow. The *Essex Chronicle* wrote "The skaters disported themselves in a gay variety of costume and the pleasure was enhanced by some good music by the town band".

* This record low of 1895 was equalled in 1982, also at Braemar .

Going nowhere. Boats frozen into the river by the parade at Burnham-on-Crouch in February 1897

A family relaxes in the Essex countryside. The photograph was taken in 1888, a cold and dismal summer.

Hail, the size of hens' eggs

24th June, 1897

A BOOK entitled *Environmental Hazards in the British Isles* shows that south and mid-Essex are the areas most prone to experience damaging hailstorms. The most terrifying example took place during the afternoon of Thursday 24th June, 1897.

It seemed like the end of the world, a maelstrom of noise, tempest and destruction dubbed by many as "Black Thursday". What had been a delightful scene of carefully nurtured crops, growing steadily in the summer sun, had become in less than 20 minutes an 'embodiment of utter desolation'. The prospects of harvest were swept away in a swathe of 100 square miles from Epping, through Ongar, Chelmsford and Colchester.

The day was hot, an oppressive 88F (31C) was recorded in Chelmsford around 2 pm with the sky an ominous copper colour, as if it were stained with ink, and reverberating to the sound of thunder.

At three o'clock, the mayor of Chelmsford had a front garden of blooming geraniums, lobelia and other flowers. Just five minutes later it was a wilderness of stalks and brown pots.

The storm approached with a roar. Lumps of ice, in places larger than hens' eggs, fell. Trees were flung from the ground, panes of glass smashed and crops beaten, pulped and pummelled into the earth. People unlucky enough to be outside were bruised and lacerated. Animals and birds succumbed to the icy bombardment, their bodies littering the fields.

The culprit was a cold front — a weather system bringing in cooler Atlantic air, displacing the tropical heat and sending columns of warm, moist air aloft to condense high in the atmosphere as ice. This grew and grew, gathering ever more layers before finally tumbling thousands of feet to earth. At the surface, down draughts of cold air brought violent squalls, hurling ice at trees, stripping the bark off their trunks and divesting them of their leafy crowns.

At Epping, the hail lay like snow and caused great damage to glass houses and windows facing west. Folk attending a jubilee dinner at Gaynes Park fled in alarm as their tent was almost carried off. The storm moved east and cattle were pelted by ice and injured at Ongar. The parish of Willingale was in a state of ruin. Everywhere, windows were smashed. Torrential rain fell as well and root crops were washed clean out of the ground. In Stondon, hailstones littered the landscape for two days and many chickens and turkeys lay dead.

At Ingatestone, the countryside in places lay under a foot of ice. Virtually every window on the north west side of houses became destitute of glass. One coachman, who had endeavoured to get his cob under the overhanging side of a house, was black and blue from the icy missiles which fell on top of him.

Nearby, at Hardings Farm and Hyde Park, 40 trees were uprooted and one hailstone measured 5.5 inches in circumference. A Member of Parliament, Mr J.L.Wharton, who visited the area later wrote: "I was astonished to see that a storm, lasting at the most for 20 minutes, could have caused such terrible injury".

The storm appeared to reach its peak at Mill Green, four miles from Chelmsford. Oaks lay like skittles in an alley, houses had their roofs entirely demolished and fruit trees looked as if they had come under rifle fire.

In the Writtle area, workers caught out in the fields had their hats cut to pieces and they were covered in bruises. One had his head cut open. The windmill was so badly damaged that the sails had to be removed. At Roxwell, 1.34 inches of rain were recorded in 30 minutes, with continuous thunder and lightning.

Chelmsford, said the *Essex Chronicle*, looked as if it had been bombarded by a hostile army. "Everything growing in the garden was remorsely cut to pieces. Flooding was severe, the railway submerged and footpaths and roadways choked with silt. The damage to Essex Industrial School was enormous and the gymnasium roof was blown away some 530 feet."

Hailstones, 6.5 inches in circumference, were measured at Little Baddow, properties were struck by lightning at Rochford and churches damaged at Colchester. Beyond the town the storm appeared to dissipate leaving just heavy rain and parting rumbles of thunder.

Estimates of the total damage of this terrifying storm were put at £200,000 and a county fund was instigated. Strenuous efforts were made to afford substantial relief to the many sufferers.

"Black Thursday" was never forgotten by the people of Essex. On this summer day in 1897, Mother Nature unleashed one of her most harrowing phenomena.

This montage of photographs shows some of the damage in Ingatestone caused by the tempest of "Black Thursday". In places the countryside lay under a foot of ice and "virtually every window on the north-west side of houses was destitute of glass".

Rowing down the High Street

29th November, 1897

THIS was "Black Monday", the day when the tide topped the defences again and produced the most remarkable and disastrous effects in Essex. All the previous Sunday afternoon, as a vigorous depression moved south-east, a south-westerly gale had blown in the county bringing down chimney pots, trees and telegraph poles. On Canvey Island, the Lobster Smack lost its roof. As the depression moved towards Denmark the wind veered to the north-west and then, during Sunday night, to the north.

Great damage was caused by the gale at Colches-ter, Halstead, Coggeshall, Chelmsford, Ingatestone, Dunmow, Ongar and many other places, but it was by the floods and high tides which accompanied the gale on the coast and the borderlands of the estuaries of the Thames, the Blackwater and the Colne, that destruction was wrought.

The sea walls were broken down in many places and it is estimated that around the Essex coast about 50,000 acres of low-lying land within the walls were flooded by sea water.

Local newspapers had some sensational material to fill their columns. The *Essex Naturalist* wrote: At

Black Monday, 1897, when the tide topped the defences and flooded Southend

Harwich by 1 pm on Monday the spray was breaking over the sea wall, and in a short time fishermen's boats, that had dragged their anchors, were tossed over the wall onto the mud. The tide continued to rise, and by two o'clock hundreds of people were on the Bath Side to witness a sight never seen before in Harwich. The whole extent of the sea wall from the continental pier to Dovercourt was one large cataract. By three o'clock, boats were being rowed a considerable distance up the main streets of Harwich. By half past three, the whole of Bath Side was flooded, in some cases the water reached to the ceilings of the lower rooms and got into the bedrooms. On Tuesday morning, people were imprisoned in their houses and baker boys could be seen rowing down the street and throwing hot rolls into the first floor windows.

"At Walton-on-the-Naze, it was of the proportion of a spring tide but "it had yet a long time to flow and there was a strong wind which tossed the backwaters into a very rough condition, forcing the waves against the walls and making breaches. At Horsey Island, of 1,000 acres, scarcely a tenth of the land escaped being submerged. At Pewit Island, the tide had complete mastery. Between Frinton and Little Holland, a wide gap was caused through which the sea rushed in an undescribable manner, drowning vast numbers of rats and ground game. At Clacton, the higher part of the beach was raised three feet by the sand left behind when the tide ebbed."

At West Mersea they had "an exciting time at what we call the 'City of Mersea', the floors of houses being covered with three or four feet of water. People had to stand on chairs and even bedridden people had to be moved."

Mersea Strood was impassable for hours. The Colne crossed the railway line between Colchester and Wivenhoe and washed away part of the embankment. That afternoon the 2.30 from Wivenhoe to Brightlingsea "was brought to a standstill, the goods break becoming derailed owing to the collapse of the line. Passengers were taken from the carriages in boats."

At Burnham-on-Crouch it was "the highest tide which has ever been known. By half past two it was pouring into the High Street like a sluice. Soon afterwards it reached the High Street by other means. Remarkable scenes were witnessed. The children of the National Schools were kept prisoners but eventually they were carried across the flood by boat. The occasional upsetting of a boat was among the most amusing scenes but there was a far more serious aspect in the amount of damage done."

Wallesea Island went under, so did a third of Foulness. Southend was flooded, an eight-oared boat was rowed up the High Street in Leigh, Canvey was submerged and all along Thames-side — at Stanford-le-Hope, Tilbury, Grays, Purfleet, Rainham and Barking — the river broke through.

No lives were lost, but personal distress was caused on a scale never known before. Public meetings were held to organise relief funds, food tickets were distributed and coal sent to those in need. A week after the 1897 inundation an engineer, appointed by the Dengie commissioners, walked from Stansgate to Middle Wick to assess the damage. He found the walls were cracked and porous to a considerable extent and recommended that "as large a gang of men as possible work uninterruptedly until the walls have been restored. Soldiers cannot remain through the winter, so navvies should be got in to continue operations".

CHAPTER THREE: 1900 - 1909

Edwardian Weather Notes

1900: Heavy snow fell on Colchester in early February, followed by frequent and copious rains. This led to the filling up of springs and ponds and, for once, the traditional "February fill dyke" proverb came true.

1901: A cold but dry year. The wells were low and water obtained from depths of 100 feet was not drinkable. According to an observer south west of Colchester the dry weather was disastrous to buildings. The sub-soil around Layer Breton church contracted and it was cracked from roof to foundation.

1902: Yet another cold year. There was a thick fog at Canvey Island in mid January. In these conditions the *Ben Mohr,* carrying cement, collided with the steamship *Banffshire.* Sea water poured into the *Ben Mohr* but the crew was rescued.

1903: Between 13th and 16th of June rain was continuous for 60 hours in the Buckhurst Hill area and totalled 4.24 inches (108mm) This is possibly the longest spell of rain recorded in Britain and it occurred in one of the driest counties. A three-week drought followed.

1904: The rainfall at Loughton during the year was 20.12 inches (514mm), compared to 38.34 inches (979mm) the previous year.

1905: The dry weather continued with villages in the Sudbury area so short of water that it had to be fetched from wells some distance away.   At Shoeburyness, only 14.6 inches (373 mm) fell in the year.

1906: Late on Christmas night, six inches of snow fell across Essex to give a festive appearance to the countryside on Boxing Day morning.

1907: In what was a cool year, the warmest day occurred late in September with 77F (25C) on the 25th, probably the latest date ever to be recorded as the "warmest day of the year."

1908: During the early morning of 24th April about a foot of snow lay in the northern part of Essex, causing much damage to trees, shrubs and all flowers. As if to compensate a burst of summer sent temperatures rising to 80 F (27C) in early October.

1909: Deep snow in early March reached nine inchesin depth in Southend. Cold weather prevailed for most of the year. Conditions in the countryside were miserable and many crops were spoilt.   At Saffron Waldon, rain was 5.3 inches above the average. On 22nd February, a large meteor was seen at around 7.30 in the evening with a luminous multicoloured train. It remained in the sky for an hour or so.

The Beeleigh Falls at Maldon in 1902. February was particularly icy.

A black, watery wasteland

12th - 20th June, 1903

THE year opened in dramatic style with a terrifying thunderstorm in January and there was flooding in the Colchester area in May, but the outstanding event took place between 12th and 20th June, with a most remarkable fall of rain. From the 13th to the 15th, some 5,348 million tons of water was precipitated - enough to provide the whole population with 25 gallons per head for more than three years. Essex took the brunt of this prodigious deluge.

Buckhurst Hill probably experienced the longest duration of rainfall in Britain, some 60 continuous hours providing 4.24 inches (108mm). The deluge extended from Saffron Walden in the north, where many approaches were cut off including the road to Little Chesterford, which was blocked by a landslip, to Southend on the Thames Estuary, where houses at Prittlefield were flooded. Here one man, concerned about the safety of his chickens, took them to bed with him.

The River Blackwater at Bocking rose to a height which exceeded anything known before. Nightwatchmen had to flee for their lives from Courtaulds Silk Works in the early hours of Tuesday 16th June when water surged in, carried off large barrels of spirit and distributed them down the valley. The works' manager, Mr Guthrie had to swim for safety when his cart began to float away as he was driving to work. A holiday was declared for the staff.

Bishops Stortford was badly inundated with the ground floors of cottages at South Mill submerged. In another street, 120 people were trapped in upper rooms and given hot coffee and food through first floor windows. At Spellbrook, homes were abandoned. Thousands of acres were submerged and one farmer lost 125 head of sheep at Parndon. Two people had a lucky escape on the River Stort when their boat was swept over South Mill Lock. They caught hold of a railing above their head and held on until rescued by lockman, Charles Pateman.

The Beeleigh Falls at Maldon looked like a miniature Niagra and the tidal river rose three feet higher than usual. Only three children out of 100 turned up for school at Cranham.

There were anxious times at Chelmsford when the River Can rose eight feet and flooded Baddow Road. The River Chelmer also overflowed and swept with great violence along Springfield Road. The corporation engaged wagons and other vehicles to carry people through the swirling water. Thousands of rats were "sent on their last account by men and boys armed with sticks".

WHO CARES FOR RAIN !
At Southend

In Laindon, rain descended in "ropes of water". Children could not get to school, workmen had to stay at home and postmen could not deliver as floodwaters reached four feet in depth. In Dunmow, those who wished to leave their homes got into dolly-tubs and ferried themselves to high ground.

Romford High Street became impassable and rate-payers were given free use of the town fire engine to pump out floodwaters. Damage ran into thousands of pounds at Ilford; the owner of a brickyard close to the church put his losses alone at £3,000. The new station goods yard was wrecked as tons of soil was washed away. Five feet of water was recorded in Southborough Road and several boats were requisitioned to rescue people and supply food to those in need. The vast mass of water looked like an inland sea at Manor Park and people gazed forlornly from top storey windows over a dreary, black, watery wasteland.

At East Ham, 790 houses had flooded while further north, at Woodford Bridge, men and women from a steam circus "were up to their armpits in their bid to extricate their caravans." The Lea Valley was under water and 500 to 600 hands of Messrs Ridley and Whitley lay idle.

Empress Avenue, Ilford during the floods of June, 1903. Several people had to be rescued by boat.

The June, 1903 floods at Abridge, near Romford. It rained for 60 hours without a break.

An "Arctic" Scene,
Jan. 16th, 1905,
Southend-on-Sea.

A short, sharp cold spell in January 1905 produced bitterly cold nights and the sea froze at Southend.

This water cart would have been a welcome sight in Lexden in the summer of 1906, when the temperatures climbed into the nineties. At Clacton, record numbers were attracted to the resort by the brilliant sunshine.

Variety with a vengeance in 1906

ESSEX, in 1906, experienced the great and infinite variety which the weather can offer — thunderstorms and tornados in August, heatwave and drought in September and a white and wonderful wintry landscape in December.

It was the ferocious series of storms which broke over the south-east on 2nd August which made the year memorable. The lightning was so vivid that crowds gathered in the streets of Braintree to witness the spectacle. At Chelmsford, the flashing was incessant for almost two hours.

The district around Great and Little Leighs suffered greatly. Hail, the size of walnuts, smashed 40 panes of glass at Leigh Priory and mangel in the fields had large chunks gourged out. Between Halstead and Sible Hedingham lightning set fire to a barn.

Damage at Rayne was confined to an area about a mile wide, but within this, a tornado had twisted through the woods, tearing down branches and sucking off the tops of mighty oak trees. One tree top was discovered 60 feet away. A semaphore was ripped off the signal box at the railway station and nearby sheds had what looked like bullet holes. Windows were shattered in houses and cottages.

Mr Harry Newman of Rayne had just retired to bed as the storm loomed. As the temperature had reached 85F that day in surburban Essex, he left his window

open but was rudely awakened by hail bombarding into the room. The icy pellets, the size of florins, quickly covered the floor,

The great heat of September, which was to be recalled in the Guinness Book of Records 90 years later, saw temperatures soar to 95F (35C) at Wanstead Flats. The parched countryside was a serious fire risk. Under the heading, The Broiling Sun, the *Essex Chronicle* related how fires swept through Hangman's Wood, near Grays, Tyrell's Heath Wood and Wanstead Flats where a thick fog hung over the district. Nine stacks were consumed by fire in east Manningfield.

There were more fires at Boreham, Canfield and Brightlingsea and the heat even affected the first partridge shoot at Moulsham Lodge when only 35 brace were bagged.

By December, it was a different story. A polar low caused heavy snow to fall across East Anglia in the last week of the month. On Boxing day at Braintree, the snow lay seven inches thick and stopped the town clock. The foxhunting meet at the Grand Hotel, Clacton had to be cancelled, many roads were blocked and trams in Colchester were unable to run. Walton-on-the-Naze and Clacton reported the heaviest snowfall for 15 years.

On New Year's Day, 1907, inquests were held at Stepney into the deaths of two women and six children who had perished in the cold weather.

Southend Pier, one of the oldest and now the longest in the country, was cut in half when the Marlborough, a Thames Conservancy vessel smashed through the pier extension during a gale on 23rd November 1908. The pier was actually extended to a mile after 1835 and rebuilt in the 1890s and the 1920s. It runs on Gothic columns of Victorian Ironwork which have been battered by frequent Channel storms but, unlike many other piers in England, it still stands to provide regular entertainment.

Snow — from April to March

THE years 1908 and 1909 are noted for their remarkable snowfalls which not only damaged telegraph lines and crops but caused loss of life throughout South East England.

On 19th April, 1908, a young man from Stratford died, his colleague surviving, when their boat overturned off Southend Pier in a blinding snowstorm. On the same day a drover, sheltering by a haystack at Arkesden, near Saffron Walden, died from exposure. This was followed, on 24th and 25th April by a blizzard which blew with "terrific force" and was accompanied by winds so strong that vessels at sea found themselves in dire trouble.

More heavy snow gave the county a Christmas Card appearance at the end of December 1908. Crowds thronged the hills carrying toboggans, and skating became a favourite pastime. Essex mailmen had to double their horses to get through to some of the more isolated villages.

Again it was grim at sea. Lifeboatmen at Clacton spent eight fruitless hours in bitter conditions, searching for a craft in distress and, on one night, Harwich and Frinton lifeboats collided in the wintry conditions. In another incident a steamer with 58 hands came ashore at Longsands.

The December snows were boosted by further falls in January and February 1909 and the beleaguered people of Essex, tiring of tobogganing and skating, looked forward to March and some warmer weather. But it snowed again. This time thick, feathery flakes hung to trees like a "great expanse of diamonds".

CHAPTER FOUR 1910 - 1919

Unrest on the weather front

1910: A cool July with temperatures often in the 50'sF. This necessitated the wearing of winter clothes, reported an observer at Brentwood.

1911: Shade temperatures in August reached 95.8F (35C). The prolonged sunshine, heat and drought meant no grass on the pastures and cows "looked like scarecrows".

1912: At Epping in 1911 only 0.5 inches (12mm) of rain fell in August. The same month in 1912 was cool and wet with 6.31 inches (161mm). Harvest operations were impeded and grain damaged.

1913: In the east of Essex, the heaviest snowfall of the "winter" fell on 12th April. A violent storm in the north of the county on 27th May with hail, the size of hens' eggs, "bruised man" and killed a number of animals and birds.

1914: On 19th June, the Roman Catholic Church at Tilbury was damaged by lightning and some of the ships in Tilbury Dock were struck. The lower part of the town was flooded and damage was reported in Grays, Purfleet and West Thurrock.

1915: The winter, 1914-15 was the wettest on record at the time, parts of Essex having 150 per cent of average rainfall. The River Chelmer flooded and meadows in the Broomfield area of Chelmsford were under water during January and February.

1916: Another wet year. Rain on 196 days at Shalford, the longest duration then recorded. There were violent gales in February and March and blinding blizzards. Snow stopped the hands of the town clock in Coggeshall on 17th February. The inclement weather continued into June when it was so cold that the temperature failed to reach 70F (21C) all month.

1917: A long cold winter, the like of which was described "of the old sort when ways were foul and milk came home frozen in pail". A boy died when he slipped through the ice of a frozen pond at Squirrels Heath in January. Sharp frosts continued into April.

1918: Heavy snow followed by a rapid thaw led to the River Roding bursting its banks in January, inundating parts of Ilford. Colchester, too, was badly flooded and, at Kelvedon, the waters "exceeded anything previously remembered". At Castle Hedingham, a six-year-old girl fell into the floodwaters and was swept away but she managed to hold on to an overhanging branch and was rescued.

1919: One of the latest snowstorms on record took place on 27th April. The Danbury district was carpeted with eight inches and a large number of fruit trees were damaged. At Braintree, part of a building collapsed under the weight of snow. All telegraphic communications to the town were lost with fallen wires festooning the roads.

Leigh-on-Sea in the springtime!   This was how the countryside looked on 24th April, 1908

When the wind backs and the glass falls, be on your guard against gales and squalls

ALTHOUGH February is, on average, one of the drier and more settled months, sometimes a succession of vicious depressions can thrust across England bringing severe weather. Such was the case in the third week of February 1910, when a series of "lows" each deeper than its precursor culminated in a great gale on Sunday 20th. Winds gusted to more than 70 mph and Essex took a pounding.

At Burnham-on-Crouch a small boat with a party of yachtsmen on board capsized, drowning two of the sailors. At Leyton a woman was severely injured by falling tiles.

Throughout the county, roads and pathways were littered with broken branches, fallen trees, far flung tiles and chimney pots. Telegraphic communications were severed at Dunmow, Colchester and Witham, the main road was partially blocked at Kelvedon and, at Southend, the conditions were tumultuous.

The Parade had been packed with people enjoying the early sunshine, but this gave way to a wind which rose to a "perfect fury." Hail and rain lashed the town and towards evening, vivid lightning and crashing thunder leant further assistance to the tumult.

The bell tower was blown down from All Saints Church, Southend, a newly-built house was partially demolished in Pall Mall and two cottages were damaged by lightning on Mersea Island. Bedroom ceilings collapsed and a woman and small boy were pulled from under the wreckage.

The scorching summer of 1911

THE kaleidoscopic weather that constantly sweeps across England occasionally becomes stuck in a repetitive pattern. The pattern in the summer of 1911 was an exotic one — weeks and weeks of Mediterranean weather.

The outstanding features were sunshine, warmth and dryness. No such rapid, or early harvest had been remembered by older farmers since 1868. At Ingatestone, by 10th August, there was no grass on the pastures and cattle were fed hay. Many failed to fatten properly.

In this memorable year, winter had made a late appearance and March "ended like a lion" with a strong wind roaring across Essex at more than 60 mph. Harwich harbour was crowded with vessels seeking shelter, including ships from the First Destroyer Flotilla. The icy wind was laden with snow and in early April even day-time temperatures failed to rise more than two degrees above freezing. On 5th April, snow lay five inches deep.

May was a warm month and rain was in short supply with only half the average at Braintree. July was outstanding. The sun beat down relentlessly for more than 10 hours a day, temperatures rose to 90F (32C) and, in Southminster only 0.19 inches (5 mm) of rain fell in the entire month.

August brought an intensification of the heat and in the Borley Green area of north Essex, a sweltering 96F (35.6C) was registered on the 9th as hot air spread north-west from the Continent. Deaths in St Osyth, Harwich, Hatfield Heath and Grays were attributed to the weather. By 9th September, the temperature was still topping 90F (32C).

However, there were a few thunderstorms to temper the heat. At Waltham Abbey, on 27th July, two huge tents were blown down and 600 children, enjoying a Sunday treat, were enveloped by the canvas. At Bannister Green, Felsted, a barn was struck by lightning "but sterling work by the Felsted School fire brigade saved the adjoining house".

The torrid heat caused a mass exodus to the coast, some 132,000 passengers leaving Liverpool Street Station during the first week of August. At Frinton-on-Sea, there were 4,000 holidaymakers on the beach and Southend pier received 6,000 during the Bank Holiday weekend.

Walton-on-the-Naze had a record season. Hundreds of people had to be turned back through lack of accommodation and people slept in bathing machines and even haylofts where they put cotton wool in their ears to keep out the beetles.

Inland, the searing heat caused many fires. Hundreds of soldiers fought a massive blaze at Warley Common, 400 tons of timber were destroyed by fire at Harwich Road, Colchester, holiday crowds helped to put out a fire at Theydon Bois and the Westcliff Scouts beat out the flames threatening a windmill at Upminster. There were fires at Shenfield Common and Panfield, where a year's crop from 240 acres was destroyed together with many farm buildings.

In October the weather pendulum swung again and in November and December, Epping endured a soaking 10 inches (250mm) of rain. In this December there were 27 days of rain in Colchester.

The Great Yeldham hailstorm

27th May, 1913

SOME hot spells provide the ingredients for a spectacular storm, and such was the case on 27th May, 1913. The temperature reached 83F (28.3C) at Southend on this day and, with fairly moist air and a cold upper atmosphere, the stage was set for one of Nature's more dramatic events - a hailstorm.

Around 4 pm the storm moved from the west-south-west, striking Great Yeldham "with a peculiar whirring noise". It lasted only eight minutes but in that time rosette-shaped hailstones, fused together to the size of chicken eggs, inflicted enormous damage. Crops were levelled to the ground, glasshouses smashed, and roofing felt cut to ribbons. Tiles and windows, shrubs and trees bore the scars of this celestial bombardment.

One farmer spoke of the toll inflicted on wildlife. He saw rooks, wood pigeons, hares, partridges, pheasants, rabbits, rats, wild ducks, farmyard fowls and cygnets lying dead. At Halstead, a hailstone was recorded as weighing a quarter of a pound and some passed straight through slated roofs.

At Dengie to the south-east, there was no hail but a thunderstorm gave over an inch of rain in under 45 minutes. These storms brought to an end an absolute drought of 15 days which had set in across Essex during May.

Troops stationed at The Royal Oak, High Beeches enjoyed a game of snowballs in March 1916 — a month of blinding blizzards.

No date appears on this photograph of the frozen sea at Walton-on-the Naze but it is certainly pre-1921 for that was the year when the Walton windmill blew down in a high storm — ironically on the same day that the Tide Mill was being dismantled. The photograph could have been taken in the late 19th century or 1917, notable for a very cold winter.

The Colchester Standard had this to say about the remarkable day in April 1919 when a civic and military church parade in the town was, at first, greeted with a blaze of sunshine. "So great was the prospect of a bright and cheerful spring day that people dispensed with their winter overcoats. As the morning progressed, however, blustering winds drove heavy clouds across the sky and the sun disappeared.

"Rain began to fall and continued with ever-increasing intensity until relieved, about five o'clock, by hail and then snow in great flakes. As the fall increased, the trees, just bursting forth into leaf gradually presented an old fashioned Christmassy appearance which looked very weird and out of place on an evening of daylight conferred by an Act of Parliament."

Much flooding occurred as a result of the fall and the photograph below shows the situation at North Station railway bridge where such a large quantity of water collected that cars had to be tugged out and people conveyed to the other side by corporation carts.

CHAPTER FIVE 1920 - 1929

A glimpse at the twenties

1920: "If the ice on a pond can bear the weight of a duck, then the winter that follows will only have sludge and muck." That November saying came true; the winter was mild and muddy. However, the summer was poor, the warmest day being around 79F (26C) on 25th May.

1921: The driest year on record. A curious fact emerged for the lack of rain lowered the mortality rate. At Chelmsford the figure was 8.8 deaths per thousand compared to 11 the previous year. It was attributed to the fact that more people were in the open, enjoying the fresh air.

The frozen sea and shoreline at Leigh-on-Sea in February 1929, when the temperature plunged to 23F during the day.

1922: After a remarkable hot spell between 20th and 24th May when temperatures approached 90F (32C), August was so chilly that upturned collars were the holiday fashion.

1923: A memorable all-night thunderstorm on 9th-10th July. An incredible 6,924 lightning flashes were recorded with 1,540 between 11 pm and midnight. At Leyton, 1.86 inches (47.5mm) of rain fell. The storm which affected the western part of the county did not clear the air for the mercury shot up to the lower 90s F, breaking temperature records for the time of the year in parts of the south-east.

1924: There was frost on 22 February nights at East Ham. In April, the temperature reached 70 F (21C) with 12 hours of sunshine on Easter Monday (21st April). Roads to the coast were jammed with motor cars.

1925: A dense fog covered London and parts of Essex between 10th - 12th January. Visibility was so poor in places that some passengers were forced to walk in front of their car. Two omnibuses collided head-on in Loughton, a charabanc returning to Chelmsford got lost in the fog and a fisherman lost his way on the mudbanks of Canvey. He was rescued by a lighthouse keeper.

1926: A short cold spell around the 17th sent the temperatures plunging to 11F (-11.7C) at Shoeburyness. After an average summer, a late burst of heat sent the temperatures soaring to 84F (29C) at Dovercourt on 20th September.

1927: A wet year. It rained on 205 days at Elsenham. A solar eclipse was unfortunately overshadowed by cloud on 29th June. The temperature at Southend on 29th June was just at freezing point, overnight. On Christmas night, rain turned to snow. It was accompanied by a gale and severe drifting occurred in west Essex. Roads were blocked for many days.

1928: The thaw of lying snow combined with heavy rain in January led to widespread flooding. About 1,000 homes were inundated in the Lea Valley and policeman "did their best in boats". The position worsened on the 6th as a deep depression moved into the North Sea causing a storm surge southwards. At Southend the tide was five feet above average and, along the Thames embankments in London, 14 people drowned.

1929: A bitter February with day-maximum temperatures of just 23F (-5C) on both the 12th and 13th. The sea froze in the creeks around the coast. March was one of the driest months of the century with only 0.02 inches (0.5mm) at Colchester. The dry weather continued until the autumn and early winter when squally and disturbed weather doubled the previous nine months' rainfall.

BEAUMONT HALL HOTEL CLACTON 26.7.21

People thronged to the seaside in the summer of 1921 and hotels were very full. Clacton, with its pier, prom, pavilion and reputation for wonderful weather, was especially popular in the "desert year". This photograph, taken on 26th July, 1921 shows some of the guests at the Beaumont Hall Hotel.

Pied Piper of Finchingfield

The desert year of 1921

IN Britain's changeable climate, air pressure constantly rises and falls and weather type does not persist for more than a few weeks. There are exceptions. In 1921, high pressure remained for week after week and gave such meagre rainfall that the land bordering the Thames Estuary recorded just 10 inches (250mm). It was the lowest annual rainfall since 1788. At Bradwell-on-Sea, June was almost rainless, but the driest place of all was Southminster with 9.94 inches (253mm). 1921 became known as "the desert year".

With a tinder-dry countryside and the temperature approaching 90 F (32C) on 10th July, there were the inevitable fires. One farmer near Braintree arrived home from market to find a wheat stack destroyed, his farmyard ruined and the flames still leaping from one building to another. The fire brigade just managed to save the farmhouse. At Star-lings Green, Clavering, a farmhouse and eight cottages went up in flames and the heat was so intense that it threatened cottages on the other side of the street. All over Essex it was the same story. There were fires at Tendring, Maldon and Hockley and, as the sun bore down onto a parched earth straining the resources of the Essex firemen, rivers ran dry and water was at a premium.

In the village of Finchingfield, the inhabitants of Howe Street had to walk half a mile to draw their water. It was impossible to keep their houses and children clean with all the dust that prevailed. One desperate cottager decided to investigate an old council bore-hole, abandoned 20 years previously, and to his astonishment he found it full of water.

Like the Pied Piper of Hamlyn he triumphantly led his thirsty neighbours and their dusty children to the well. Carrying tins, pans, kettles, pails and buckets they walked in a long line behind the hero of Finchingfield to the old well.

Heat breeds violent storms

THE weather in the second week of July, 1923 hit the headlines for its heat. After a disappointingly cool June, a sudden burst of summer saw the temperature soar to more than 90F (23C) - destined to be a record high for the decade.

On Tuesday 10th July, a woman was found dead on a footpath near Ten Acre Field, Stisted where she had been picking peas. The footpath was in the full glare of the sun and she had been overcome by the intense heat. A man was discovered dead in a field at West Hanningfield — from sunstroke.

The hot weather triggered off violent thunderstorms. Three dogs died in a blazing barn by the White Hart, Hatfield Heath when thatched stables were set on fire by lightning on 10th July. A farmhouse at Pilgrims Hatch, near Brentwood was also struck leaving two gaping holes in the wall.

At Laburnham Cottages in South Weald, the lightning caused havoc. Large quantities of plaster and soot "swirled about rooms where a butler and chauffeur were sleeping". At Rainham, a hole was torn in the roof of a house, at Fyfield, a huge poplar in the Rev. A.J. Challis' garden was split right down the middle, at Saffron Walden General Hospital a tree was struck near the nurses' home and at Hatfield Broad Oak a tree shattered and wooden missiles were hurled violently around a garden.

August mustered a temperature of 85F (29C) but September was cool.

A mighty splash, Clacton-on-Sea.

A mighty splash. This is the other face of Clacton-on-Sea — the one that provides spectacular waves and sends holidaymakers scurrying for shelter as the sea swirls over the promenade and splashes into the town itself. The coastline between Harwich and Clacton is largely formed of low cliffs of London clay, varying in height from 70 ft to less than 40 ft and, over the years, they have yielded readily to wave attack.

Ice, blizzards, gales and floods

Dec 1927 - Jan 1928

IN the late evening of Christmas Day, 1927, there began a snowstorm to rival the greatest blizzard of the nineteenth century. By Boxing Day, villages were marooned, vehicles buried and gales were lashing the coast. Early in the New Year, the snows thawed. The thaw was accompanied by heavy rain and the North Sea, anxious to get in on the act, produced a tidal surge which played havoc all along the coast and river estuaries.

December had been mainly dry and cold — the daytime temperature on the 18th was only 28F (-2C). An incursion of mild air, however, led to glazed frost on the 21st causing great difficulties for pedestrians and vehicles. The mild weather persisted but on the 25th a fairly deep area of low pressure developed at the mouth of the Channel and cold north-east winds were brought into contact with warm southerlies from the Bay of Biscay.

Those brave enough to walk off the excesses of Christmas dinner received a soaking but the continuous rain first turned to sleet and then, by degrees, to snow. As the wind strengthened to gale force, a fully-fledged snowstorm raged across the county on Christmas night and continued throughout Boxing Day.

As dawn broke, roads were buried to the tops of hedges. The railway line between Bishops Stortford and Dunmow was snowed up at Hockerill Halt and hundreds of holiday travellers were stranded. A lady was found exhausted and waist deep in snow at Dirty Dick's Corner near Saffron Walden.

The communities of Bardfield and Finchingfield were isolated for nearly a week. Great piles of letters and parcels accumulated in Braintree Post Office and, in the same town, beer supplies ran dry. Meanwhile the height of the drifts increased, reaching a depth of 15 feet near Wethersfield. Main roads were blocked and Saffron Walden, Dunmow, Halstead and Sible Hedingham were completely cut off.

Along the coast, the north-east gale battered and pounded the promenades, At Walton East, beach huts were torn up, the parade was littered with lumps of masonry and the South Beach groyne was all but washed away. Those who dared to watch the sea bursting over the front were treated to a magnificent spectacle. At Frinton, where higher waves "could not be recalled", landslips occurred as the cliffs gave way.

The New Year, 1928, brought a change in the weather but not for the better, for a sudden swing from frost to thaw was accompanied by heavy rain and gales. Rivers throughout Essex burst their banks and hundreds suffered from burst pipes and flooding from within.

As a deep low moved south-east across Scotland and then the North Sea, the situation worsened. A severe gale blew from the north-west, piling up waters in its narrowing southern end adjacent to Essex. With a high tide, and rivers already at bursting point, the stage was set for the worst tidal flooding for 50 years. Sea levels were now six feet above those predicted.

So great was the pressure of water at Maldon and Heybridge that the river wall broke and the torrents swept in. One man walking along Well Terrace, Maldon, was swept off his feet and dashed against an iron fence. He managed to cling on and save himself. The water flowed along the streets with a muffled roar. Doors burst open and chairs, kitchen utensils and toys came floating down the roads. In one house, 17 women and children escaped to an upstairs room. They were refugees from surrounding bungalows.

The power house supplying Maldon with electricity was invaded by the tide. Great waves lifted the barge, *Mermaid,* on top of the Corporation Quay and, at Wivenhoe, the tide exceeded all previous records as it reached the gasworks, put out the boilers and sent a plume of steam 100 feet into the sky.

The roar of the waters attracted many spectators who found they were unable to return to their homes. The 400-ton yacht, *Rosenbelle,* in dry dock was soon afloat, Fingringhoe flour mill was badly damaged, an explosives factory at Bramwell Island was inundated and Brightlingsea was littered with fallen slates and tiles, telephone and electricity wires and even the remains of chimney stacks.

Wethersfield, blocked a week earlier by huge snowdrifts, was impassable again. So many roads were blocked in Bishops Stortford that bus passengers had to disembark and walk. The old windmill at Great Bardfield which had stood for nearly a century was razed to the ground. A man died at Buckhurst Hill when a tree toppled down on top of him.

Along the banks of the Thames the abnormal tides created havoc. 800 houses were damaged at West Ham and 1,600 families needed special assistance. In order to save the electricity supply at West Ham, the assistant engineer at the pumping station stood for five hours in flood water, running the risk of an explosion. So quickly did the waters rise that in London, 14 people were drowned in basement rooms.

A photograph taken on the last day of 1927 at Finchingfield. It shows the cutting beyond Justices Hill looking towards Wethersfield.

Clearing a way over the hill at Beslyns Road, Great Bardfield in December, 1927.

Grange Hill, Coggeshall in January 1928 - flooding in the wake of the Boxing Day blizzard.

Another view of the floods at Coggeshall — and more reliable transport!

Fourteen people, including four young sisters, were drowned in their basement homes and hundreds more were made homeless along the length of the grey, swollen River Thames in the floods of January 1928.

A photograph taken in July, 1929 behind Choppings Mill, Colchester. The children are enjoying a surprise warm spell of weather during a not particularly memorable summer.

Skating on the River Colne, 1929

During February, 1929 a vast, anticyclone over north-east Europe drove bitterly cold air across Essex. On the 11th, in Ilford, the mercury stood at just 18F (-8C) and for the next week even maximum readings never rose above freezing point.

Snow, up to four inches deep, carpeted the ground in many parts of the county but this was a thin layer compared to the reputed six feet of snow which fell in 24 hours on Dartmoor.

The month as a whole averaged at, or just below freezing, making it the fifth coldest February this century behind 1947, 1986, 1963 and 1956. Skaters enthusiastically took to the frozen ponds, lakes, and rivers; our photograph shows two young men and a dog enjoying the freedom of the River Colne. It was taken on 29th February, possibly early in the morning before the rest of the river's customers arrived. In the nineteenth and early twentieth century, skating on the Colne was a popular winter sport. during icy spells.

CHAPTER SIX 1930 - 1939

Window on the Thirties

1930: January was mild, wild and blustery with a great gale on Sunday 12th. It was one of the worst of the century. Winds reached 80 mph and there was considerable structural damage, fallen trees and injury. In Bocking, a garage, 105 feet long and 35 feet wide was demolished. In Widford, an omnibus was trapped by fallen trees to the front and rear.

1931: A cold year. Heavy snow fell on 9th March. In the Brentwood area many roads were impassable and temperatures remained below freezing by day. There were many accidents, including an overturned lorry, carrying sheep, at White's Bridge, Billericay. The sheep were found, unhurt, standing on the inside of the roof of the upside down lorry.

1932: The winter was the driest at Colchester for more than 30 years. In a summer not noted for its overall warmth, a blaze of heat sent temperatures to record levels in Essex on 19th August. At Halstead, 97F (36.1C) was measured. Several bathers died including a man in Pitmore Lock, Lamarsh and another at Nazeing. On Sunday 21st August, a terrific thunderstorm broke over Dunmow at 3.30 am. Lightning tore a hole in the chimney stack of a bakery shop in North Street.

1933: A dry and warm year. Only 11.33 inches (289mm) of rain was measured at Wickham Bishops, half the annual average. Whitsun was gloriously sunny on 3rd-5th June, with an average of 13 hours' sun. There were localised storms and on 19th June lightning damaged houses in Plaistow and East Ham. Moreton granary was badly wrecked and, at Shalford, a lady was knocked senseless when lightning struck her cottage. Late July saw the start of a heatwave and 92 F (33.3C) was recorded at Tolleshunt D'Arcy. There were nine successive days in the eighties. August was an outstanding month. The year ended with air frost on 23 nights in December.

1934: A year with some warm months, including December, which was the warmest for more than two hundred years. Parts of Essex failed to register a frost and there were 20 days with temperatures above 50F (10C).

1935: A deep depression moved across Ireland and severe gales developed on its southern edge, sweeping across Essex on Monday and Tuesday 16th-17th September. The Braintree motor mail van had its passage blocked by fallen trees and morning deliveries were held up for several hours. At Southend, windows were blown in and the steam boat from Calais could not put in at the pier head. It turned back and, in heavy seas, went on to Tilbury. All along the coast the gale wrought havoc, with several small vessels sunk at Walton. At Colchester more than 1,000 telephone wires were damaged and, at Waltham Cross, a 16-year-old boy was killed when he was blown off his bicycle in front of a tram.

1936: This year brought the first of three successive poor Easters with sleet and snow. The weather was kind for the annual Burnham Regatta on 12th August but in early September there were violent thunderstorms with lightning damage. The Essex Chronicle reported that the chimney of Colchester Barracks was cleft in two by lightning on Saturday 5th September. One soldier dashed for the door, another hid beneath a bed and a third made an exit through a window. Two days later gales swept the country and played havoc with the fruit crop. One workman in Westcliff was badly injured when he was blown 40 feet from a roof and another person in Ilford was struck by an advertisement hoarding.

1937: A wet year with 29.8 inches (762mm) of rain. The Chelmsford Races were abandoned on 3rd April because rain had made training sessions dangerous and many horses were unfit. Easter was wintry with Good Friday, 26th March, bringing snow.

1938: A year which boasted two exceptionally mild months, March and November. In Essex, the temperature reached 69F (20.6C) and in London 70F (21C) on 5th November. The unseasonably warm weather continued into December but on the 16th an ominous backing of the wind to the east brought bitterly cold air in from north-west Europe. By the 18th the temperatures, even during the day, failed to rise above freezing. Snow fell thickly and on Christmas Day, Essex presented a festive picture. Snow was almost a foot deep in Romford on Boxing Day.

1939: This was a very wet year. At Colchester 31.6 inches (807mm) was recorded. This still remains the greatest since observations began in 1887. October was particularly wet — eight inches (200mm) being measured in the gauge.

The Loughton High Road on 18th June, 1930 was passable — but only just.

80mph wind fells many trees

NORTH EAST Essex suffered badly from the severe gale which hit the county on 12th January 1930. High winds, in excess of 80 mph, felled many trees and structural damage was extensive but the *County Standard* reported that there was no injury to life or limb.

The district of St Osyth, Walton and Frinton took the brunt of the storm. Chimney stacks at the Marine Hotel, Walton crashed through the roof, a small lock-up garage was lifted off the ground,

greenhouses were shattered and a man at Wick, seeing poplars bending like rainbows as he walked home, decided that discretion was the better part of valour and traversed an adjoining field.

"Weeley experienced the full force of this violent gale and casualties were numerous," wrote the *Standard* . "Happily most of them were not serious, but the mortality among trees and wireless poles was alarming".

This photograph appeared in the Evening Gazette, Colchester on 5th December, 1936 when the Essex coast was hit by "the worst floods ever known." The car belongs to the newspaper's cameraman Douglas Went, who left it in a rather vulnerable position at Brightlingsea and then went off to take pictures of the damage. He must have had a nasty shock when he returned and we wonder if the Gazette was able to foot the bill for flood damage?

The culprit was an abnormally high spring tide, banked up by high winds which caused great havoc in Jaywick, St Osyth, Wivenhoe and Rowhedge. There was no damage at Clacton but the sea was level with the lower promenade and that attracted hundreds of sightseers.

At Wivenhoe, the scene on the quayside was pathetic. The Gazette wrote: "People stood in the bitter cold wind with doors open and no fires, wringing out clothes full of freezing water". The gas works at Wivenhoe were flooded and furnaces put out. Several people were marooned in their bedrooms and in one bungalow three small children were rescued.

DAILY SKETCH

ALL THE HOLIDAY NEWS AND PICTURES

WIRELESS: P. 14

No. 9,124   MONDAY, AUGUST 1, 1938   ONE PENNY

Two Kinds Of Flood!

A DELIGHTFUL thing about our climate is its habit of contrast—provided you are on the right side of it. Just look at those teeming thousands on the sands at Southend . . . happy, care-free Londoners they are—including that fellow in the bowler hat.

They basked in the sun that flooded southern England, while those who went north were flooded out.

Campers and caravaneers (instance the oval

In a somewhat cloudy summer, crowds made the most of a hot sunny interlude which, for once, occurred during the August Bank Holiday. The Daily Sketch picture was taken on Sunday 31st July 1938 at Southend on a day which enjoyed temperatures in the eighties. Thousands slept on the beach and around the cliffs during the holiday weekend because all hotels and guest houses were fully booked. The hot weather ended on a thundery note.

CHAPTER SEVEN 1940 - 1949

The war years and beyond

1940: A severe January with average temperatures below freezing throughout the county. It was possible to walk across the frozen creeks at West Mersea. Ice floes sunk one boat and blasting pellets were used at Wivenhoe in an attempt to break the ice to allow spratting smacks and a ferry to leave the quay. A heavy snowstorm on Friday 16th January continued for two more days. In June, sunshine averaged nearly 10 hours a day for the Battle of Britain.

1941: A cold winter with plenty of snow. The highest temperature in January was only 46F (8C). On 26th July, a remarkable 3.9 inches (99mm) of rain fell in less than two hours at Writtle.

1942: The third successive cold and snowy winter. In Romford snow fell on 17 days in January and 19 in February. Spring was notable for a 30-day absolute drought over Essex from 10th April - 10th May. Just after 6 pm on 14th June a violent thunderstorm with a deluge of hail swept over east Essex and south-east Suffolk. In places hail was a foot deep and several inches remained the next day. At Harwich, six barrage balloons were struck by lightning and there was extensive damage to crops.

1943: The winter was mild, the spring dry and a hot spell at the end of July sent temperatures soaring close to 90F (32C) on the 31st. However, the warmth was abruptly terminated by a squally line of thunderstorms bringing in fresher Atlantic air.

1944: The second consecutive dry spring. 29th May was the hottest day of the year with a scorching 90F (32C) at East Ham. The summer that followed was disappointing. Christmas was cold and foggy but beautiful rime accretions covered trees and shrubs in the Chelmsford district on the 27th.

1945: Remarkable variations in the weather. January was bitterly cold with snow lying for more than half of the month and February was so mild that the temperature reached 61F (16C) on the 18th. On 6th August, a most violent thunderstorm hit Clacton. The day was warm and humid, reaching 81F (27C) and during the evening a brief storm occurred. Vivid, continuous lightning accompanied a torrential downpour with heavy hail. An intense fall of rain measured 0.8 inches (20mm) in just 15 minutes.

1946: Summer arrived early with the temperature reaching nearly 80F (27C) on 4th April in south Essex but most of the year was disappointing and especially wet in November. During the month a south-west gale with heavy rain and thunderstorms led to flooding at Jaywick where the sea defences were also breached.

1947: "As the day lengthens so the cold strengthens" goes an old weather saying. This year it came true. Late January saw start of a severe cold spell which carpeted the ground with snow for six weeks. The village of Beaumont, between Harwich and Clacton was entirely isolated by deep drifts and German POWs helped to clear a way through the snow. The tidal reaches on the River Blackwater froze over and so did the sea at Southend. In March there was a violent blizzard and, in the thaw that followed, Chelmsford experienced its worst floods since 1888. The summer was as brilliant as the winter was icy and, as late as 15th September, temperatures in Southend reached 84F (29C).

1948: Another late winter. Snowstorms on 20th-22nd February gave nine inches of powdery snow with deep drifts and a day maximum on the 20th of only 26F (-3C) in Romford. Brilliant sunshine in the days that followed warmed up the land and by 9th March the mercury exceeded 70F (21C), the earliest known date for such a high value. A hot spell in July registered 92F (33C) at Halstead on the 30th.

1949: After an exceptionally sunny February, March roared in like a lion with a severe northerly gale and the resultant sea surge and high tide caused flooding as far up river as Battlesbridge on the Crouch and in the Brightlingsea area. Easter was the warmest on record, reaching the mid-eighties in London and not far behind in Essex. Between Friday 15th and Monday 18th April, 44 hours of sunshine were recorded. The summer was long, warm and sunny and reached a peak in early September when, on the 5th, Maldon recorded 91F (33C).

Royal Corinthian Yacht Club, Burnham, in the 1940 freeze-up

Ice age returns — but it's a secret!

THE bitter winter of 1939-40, at the beginning of the war, was the one no-one talked about! Certainly all news of the big freeze-up was censored by newspapers for 15 days for fear the information would be useful to the enemy. In fact Essex was no different to the rest of Britain and Europe which shivered in one of the coldest spells since 1895.

Very cold conditions with some snow set in at the end of December 1939. The cold intensified the following month and by the middle of January, Essex was in the grip of one of its most severe frosts of the century. Lying snow, blown off the fields, caused drifts on country roads which were several feet deep. Rivers froze over including a seven mile stretch between Leigh and Shoeburyness in the Thames Estuary. Here, barges were frozen up and the ice extended more than a quarter of a mile from the water's edge. So thick was the ice that children actually skated on the foreshore.

Plumbers worked 24 hours around the clock as temperatures dropped to below freezing. Ice clogged up toilet cisterns and living room fires supplying hot water were ineffective because water tanks froze

solid in attics. In some streets in the county stand-pipes were erected so people could fill containers with water for use in the house.

Snowdrifts posed severe hazards on the roads. On the main road out of Braintree to Chelmsford, ten feet of snow blocked the way at Little Waltham. Several drivers were stranded, including Rab Butler MP.

A letter in the *Essex County Standard* at Colchester, which was held until the censorship period ended, compared the snowstorm of 1940 with that of 1881. The correspondent wrote: "The scenes on 18th January reminded me of that great occasion 59 years earlier when the snow towered higher than houses in Elmstead known as Sage Villas. On that occasion the mail driver from Walton-on-the-Naze arrived at 8.20 pm having abandoned his mail cart in the vicinity of Frating Brook."

In East London and Metropolitan Essex, January 1940 was on average the coldest since records began in 1841. It was certainly colder than any month since February 1895 but this particular winter for many weeks was a secret!

This atmospheric photograph, taken by an American airman stationed near Colchester shows a bleak day in January 1945 when the skies were still heavy, the roads wore a thin but crisp coating of snow, there was no traffic in sight — even on one of the busiest junctions — and a lone, huddled figure was making her way home, carefully but anxiously.

Weathermen in 1943 rarely gave advance warnings of likely structural damage when a gale was expected. Even if such forecasts were possible, there was little the people of Southend could have done about the gale that struck the town on 31st January 1943 when several homes were badly damaged. Photograph shows the back gardens of houses in Victoria Road, Southchurch littered with broken fences, tiles and debris of all kinds.

The bleak, snowy winter of 1947

Seven weeks of ice

FACED with a strike in January by road haulage workers, which left much of the country without meat and other food stuffs, and with fuel still scarce as a legacy of the war, the British people and especially the poor, hoped for a mild winter. Hopes were dashed when it turned out to be one of the bleakest and snowiest ever known.

The people of Essex, particularly, thought they had escaped the worst when most of January passed with little sign of bad weather. As the month entered its third week, winds turned to the east — a direction that indicated an onslaught from Siberia.

Late on Sunday 19th January, weather observer, Mr T.W. Partis of Plaistow wrote in his diary that a moderate easterly wind had set in by the end of the day and the temperature had struggled to reach 37F (3C). This was the prelude to two months of hardship.

As the freeze intensified, ice floes formed on the River Crouch, chaos and power cuts swept across the county and traders in Southend carried on by candlelight. On Thursday 23rd January, snow showers fell from clouds blowing in from the north-east and the temperature remained below freezing. By Saturday the wind was stronger and the next day, Sunday 26th January, it was spiteful. It blew at gale force and the snow was heavy. The tidal reaches of the River Blackwater froze over and at Chelmsford, the Rivers Chelmer and Can also iced up.

The Red Lion at Thorrington became a travellers' rest for 50 people journeying on the London-to-Clacton coaches which became stuck in snowdrifts six feet deep. People took to skis in Boxted and Colchester.

The Rev Alfred Kibble, rector of Little Bentley lost his way in the blizzard in Regents Park and plunged into a lake where he stood for an hour in icy water five feet deep before being rescued.

On Tuesday 28th January, the country was paralysed by 27 degrees of frost (-15C) and an intense blizzard gave two inches of snow in 15 minutes near Plaistow. At 6 pm the temperature in London stood at a numbing 15 F (-9C) and visibility in Metropolitan Essex was reduced, in places, to just 20 yards.

Next morning, parts of Essex were under a five-inch blanket of snow, and this was only the beginning. Snow fell on each of the next nine days and, almost without exception, the sun failed to appear. In central Essex, between nine inches and a foot of level snow covered the ground. Snowploughs took to the streets.

On the night of 18th January, the temperature dropped to a bone-chilling -5F (-20C) at Writtle, near Chelmsford. At Maldon Grammar School only 145 out of 330 pupils turned up on one day. It was the same in schools throughout the county.

Beaumont, near Thorpe-le-Soken, was isolated for nearly three days by snowdrifts 10 to 15 feet deep. Not until the evening of 29th January was the community relieved when some 150 German prisoners of war from a nearby camp joined locals in digging their way out. Two days later more POWs helped to clear Chelmsford's New Writtle Street football ground.

Nearly all of February was intensely cold, snowy and exceptionally dull. For a fortnight between 11th and 25th the temperature did not get higher than freezing point by day or night. The temperature fell to 8F (-14c) at Plaistow on the 14th. Halstead reported 29 degrees of frost (-16C) - the coldest since 1902. Even though the sun appeared for the first time for 17 days, it remained bitterly cold and the sea froze over again at Southend.

The relentless cold weather claimed many victims. Marconi's factory at Chelmsford was forced to lay off 2,300 workers and C.H. Bernard and Sons, naval clothiers of Harwich made more redundant. Throughout the county, dole queues became longer and longer.

The coal shortage hit churches. The congregation at Chelmsford Cathedral shivered in the pews while wardens made sure doors and windows were shut tight. Not a single piece of coal was available for heating. Cinemas put back their opening performances to 4 pm, hairdressers cancelled all permanent waving appointments and the train service along Southend pier was severely curtailed.

The extreme cold over Eastern Europe drove a pair of waxwings westwards. They stopped off in a garden at Braintree but after a few days feeding off berries, they were chased away by a jealous mistle thrush.

March came in like a shivering lamb. The first few days were sunny but it remained exceptionally cold. Weatherman Partis wrote in his Plaistow diary: "Walked up the Dock Road about 4.30 pm. Wind was east, blowing at 50 mph. Temperature was 31 F and it was snowing exceptionally heavily. It was all I could do to walk against it. It was snowing so heavily I could hardly see, or breathe."

On Saturday 8th March, the winds turned to the south-west and it became less cold. On the next day, 46F (8C) was reached and rain fell in the evening.

The unusual spectacle of a frozen flood at Woodford on March 15th, 1947.

Winter, however, had not yet finished with this extraordinary year for cold air surged back and it snowed yet again.

By Tuesday 11th March the temperature was still only 33F (0C) and the next day rain fell heavily at a temperature below freezing. Roads now became coated with a lethal varnish of ice.

On Thursday 13th March the ground in London's East End was clear of snow for the first time since 23rd January and a high of 49F (9C) was attained, but yet again, cold northerly winds gathered forces for a new onslaught. This time five inches of snow fell on 15th March.

The winter's power was gradually weakening and to finish it off a warm Atlantic system stormed in with winds up to 98 mph. A trail of havoc was left in Essex but warm air was now flooding the county, melting the snow and ice, and the temperature reached a commendable 57F (14C).

Few people who were living in Essex at the time will forget the winter and spring of 1947. Nor will they forget the splendid hot summer which followed.

It is unlikely that the Anchor Hotel, Burnham had any guests on the night of 28th January — apart from those who were stranded in the vicinity. The whole area was isolated by snow, blown into huge drifts by the wind from the sea.

As the snow and ice of 1947 rapidly thawed, a new but familiar menace hit many towns and villages in Essex — floods. The picture above was taken on Turnford High Road, Waltham Cross, where the AA had helpfully placed diversion signs on March 13th. Some traffic, however, didn't bother about water near the town centre — negotiating floods was simple.

The legendary winter of 1947 with its extreme February temperatures, frozen seas, raging blizzards, unbelievable drifts, spring snowfalls and great storms had its final fling on 15th March, thereafter a warm Atlantic system finally flushed out the cold air. But, in the wake of the rapid thaw which accompanied the warm air, came the inevitable floods, more havoc and a new misery.

In Chelmsford, floodwater surged into buildings, including the hospital where staff, holding hurricane lamps, had to wade through deep muddy water in order to rescue supplies from the basement. It was the same story in most Essex towns and villages as the photographs (above) of Benfleet and (right) Manningtree clearly show.

EVERY Picture tells a story!

Fleeing from the waves — in summer

9th August, 1948

FOLLOWING the disastrous flooding of 1947, Jaywick again found itself in a potentially calamitous situation at the beginning of August, 1948.

Holidaymakers had enjoyed a bumper Bank Holiday on Monday the 2nd with midnight bathing and people sleeping on the beach. The following weekend brought the unusual combination of a fierce north-westerly wind combined with a high 'spring' tide and heavy seas broke over the sea wall. Property valued at £1 million was quickly engulfed.

The seaside chalets were full and, at 3 am, a policeman's whistle alerted them to the danger. Many escaped but other holidaymakers were stranded and had to be rescued by policemen in bathing costumes.

Children enjoyed the novelty of the situation but most people were terrified by the experience. Mrs Brooker of Walthamstow was awakened by a noise like thunder and looked out of the bedroom window to see a huge wave crash over the roof. Mrs Fisher of Attleborough was woken up by screams and was aware of her bungalow rocking like a boat. Baby David Thompson was nearly lost when he floated away down the street but was rescued safely after swallowing a lot of water.

In all, 2,000 holidaymakers were hurriedly evacuated and a special train was laid on to take the majority back to London, some most disgruntled as they had only arrived in Jaywick on Saturday.

The seaside chalets at Jaywick were full of holidaymakers when the sea came over the wall with enormous life-threatening waves. More than 2,000 people were able to escape, some running along the beach, ankle deep in foaming water.

The landlady of the Barge Inn at Battlesbridge, Mrs Sarah White, aged 72 said that in her experience only two winters had gone by without floods. In 1949 the village was under water on two occasions — lst March and 25th October. Picture shows two buses battling with the latter inundation.

Record high tide at Clacton, 1949

"MORE than 1,000 workmen and soldiers are struggling against time to repair 60 breaches in the sea walls before the big March tides arrive in ten days' time." This was the dramatic account in the *Essex Chronicle* following a 70-mph gale on 1st March, 1949 which caused sensational tides to "pile up" around the Essex coast.

The floods swept up the River Crouch and Battlesbridge, 15 miles inland was inundated. The villagers were "astounded by the swiftness with which the water rose and swept into their homes." The tide at Clacton was 10 inches higher than the highest ever recorded and, along Thameside, came within a few inches of the top of the walls protecting the big oil refineries.

Landlady of the Barge Inn at Battlesbridge, Mrs Sarah White said the floods had never been so bad. "It came pouring in the six doors, back and front. The chicken house was swept away and chicks were swimming around, searching in vain for dry land."

At Frinton and Walton, beach huts were washed away and the thorny question of inadequate defences in the wake of such angry tides was raised again. "What will happen to Essex if a great storm surge coincides with an exceptional high tide?"

The answer was now just four years away...

Cyclists splash bravely through the flooded streets of Burnham-on-Crouch after the gale of 1st March, 1949 had whipped the tide into one of the highest ever known. At noon, sandbags were placed at the entrance to the jetties and right along the front but to no avail, for the water invaded the High Street shops in the afternoon.

The glorious summer of 1949

The brilliant summer of 1947 was followed, two years later, by another glorious year which began as early as February when parts of Essex enjoyed 100 hours of sunshine.

The Easter weekend was particularly outstanding. In the towns and villages around the Thames Estuary the thermometer soared to 85F (29C). Such heat in April had not been known for 150 years. On Easter Saturday, 16th April, 12 hours of sun was enjoyed, on Easter Sunday more than 11 hours and Easter Monday, 10.9 hours.

Fine summer weather blessed the county from mid-June to September offering, on average, five hours of sunshine a day and straining the resources of the Essex Fire Brigade who attended scores of forest and heathland fires. In many areas rivers ran dry and water was rationed.

September brought an Indian summer. On the 4th, temperatures reached 89F (31C) at Plaistow and Barking and, by the 12th, Essex was still basking in the eighties. Even on 3rd October, 79F (26C) was observed.

Hoar frosts occurred in December, 1951 as a prelude to a severe spell in January which was repeated in March, 1952. This picture was taken at South Park, Ilford on 12th December.

CHAPTER EIGHT 1950 — 1959

Dismal summers of the fifties

1950: After a spring-like temperature of 64F (18C) on 21st April, residents of south Essex woke up to six inches of snow on the morning of 25th April. December was snowy, especially in Romford where it was observed on 18 days and the month was the coldest December since 1890.

1951: A cold front moved south-east across Essex on 1st January and, in many parts of the county, it was completely dark at noon. Heavy snow followed. On the 19th July, Southend was the warmest place in Britain for the year with 86F (30C). October brought some unusually cold nights and many streams were frozen.

1952: On the 21st March the temperature reached 60F (16C) with spring well under way. But the weather pendulum swung and by the 29th, a fierce snowstorm swept Essex. It was the latest date in the calendar year for sub-zero temperatures since 1806. Summer did make an appearance, the temperature reaching 90F (32C) on the 1st July but winter returned early and snow fell on 11 days in November. There was dense fog between 5th and 8th December.

1953: The year which was dominated by the infamous East Coast floods of 31st January but in February and March there was a 34-day absolute drought! Sadly, it rained heavily on 2nd June — Coronation Day — and there were bitterly cold northerly winds, more suited to March. On 10th August, a whirlwind caused considerable mischief in Southend.

1954: Sandwiched in the middle of an unsettled spell, 1st December was a glorious day with seven hours' sunshine - far better than many days of the preceding summer which was one of the worst of the century.

1955: On Tuesday 17th May, the southerly wind veered northerly, becoming squally. Heavy snow fell for a while in the Barking and Dagenham district and, at 7 pm, the temperature was only 35F (2C). Snow lay deeply in parts of the Midlands and northern England.

1956: The year was notable for a severely cold February and one of the worst July gales ever experienced. At Shoeburyness on the 29th, the wind averaged 60mph with a gust to 77mph. There was widespread damage.

1957: The warmest March on record. Only one day during the month had a maximum below 50F (10C).

1958: The old weather proverb "a green Christmas, a white Easter" came true. Snow fell on Good Friday, 4th April and was several inches deep on Easter Saturday. A somewhat cool and showery summer followed, culminating in the sensational storm of 5th September. It was one of the wettest years ever known at Shoeburyness with 29.7 inches of rain (758 mm).

1959: Nature made amends for a cold and damp decade and everyone forgave her. It was a glorious summer which continued until October. September was virtually rainless with only 0.08 inches (2mm) at Romford and 80F (27C) was achieved on 3rd October. There was a national water shortage — even in the Highlands of Scotland !

The great London 'smog' kills 4,000

Hundreds of Essex people living near the industrial connurbation of the Thames Embankment were among the 4,000-plus people who died as a result of the "great smog" of 5th-8th December 1952. It was the greatest mass killer of the twentieth century.

The first indication that a genuine "Victorian pea-souper" was to hit London and its environs was given on the wireless on 4th December. The next night was chaotic. Road and rail traffic was cancelled and dockland workers couldn't even see their own feet.

Those living near, or passing by, factories and power houses suffered violent fits of coughing for the fog contained pockets of sulphur dioxide and associated gasses emanating from chimneys. People suffered an irritation of the respiratory system which led to heart failure. Many animals were asphixiated.

The *Ilford Guardian* reported that home comfort was not even possible because families sat looking at empty grates. Coal merchants had been unable to make deliveries through the dark and murky streets.

One woman spent three hours travelling to a maternity hospital by ambulance. It was guided through the Ilford streets by a nurse who walked in front with a torch. The next day a little girl was born.

'The best efforts of men have so far preserved us'

THE Essex River Board was the organisation responsible for the defences of the county. Established in April 1952 it had in its care, 592 miles of main river, 402 miles of common watercourses, more than 300 miles of sea and tidal river defences and 500 tidal sluices. It met for the first time in July 1952.

In August of that year, heavy rainfall brought disaster to two small Devon villages, Lynton and Lynmouth, when the rivers burst their banks and swept down surrounding hills. The torrents swamped the area so quickly that victims had no time to flee their homes. They were buried beneath a flow of mud, rocks and debris.

The *Essex Weekly News* in describing the disaster and supporting the Flood Relief Fund said there were deep reasons why a helping hand should stretch from east to west. "The seaboard of Essex is some 400 miles long. No less than 300 miles of it is protected by tidal embankment. Disaster in Devon is a reminder that only constant maintenance of the sea wall stands between us and disaster by flood. The best efforts of men have so far preserved us. It may not always be so. In responding generously to the West Country's Appeal Essex gives thanks for life itself.

On 31st January 1953 — six months later — the sea wall gave way.

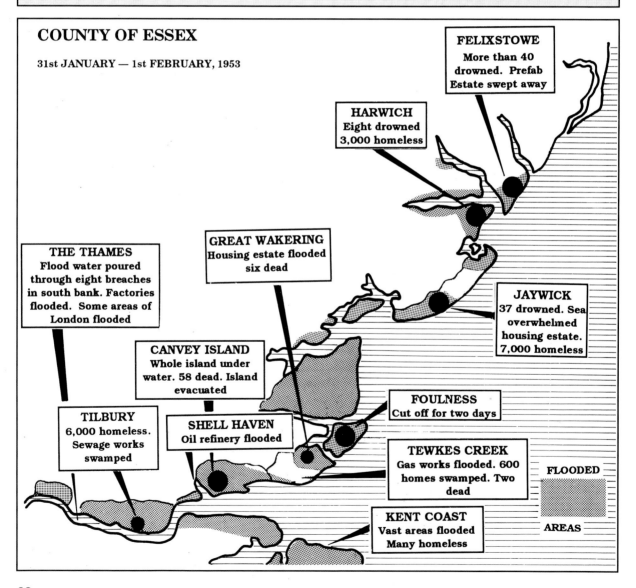

COUNTY OF ESSEX

31st JANUARY — 1st FEBRUARY, 1953

FELIXSTOWE
More than 40 drowned. Prefab Estate swept away

HARWICH
Eight drowned 3,000 homeless

THE THAMES
Flood water poured through eight breaches in south bank. Factories flooded. Some areas of London flooded

GREAT WAKERING
Housing estate flooded six dead

JAYWICK
37 drowned. Sea overwhelmed housing estate. 7,000 homeless

CANVEY ISLAND
Whole island under water. 58 dead. Island evacuated

FOULNESS
Cut off for two days

TILBURY
6,000 homeless. Sewage works swamped

SHELL HAVEN
Oil refinery flooded

TEWKES CREEK
Gas works flooded. 600 homes swamped. Two dead

KENT COAST
Vast areas flooded Many homeless

FLOODED

AREAS

113 drown in great tidal surge

January 31st — February 1st, 1953

THIS was the most catastrophic British weather event of the century. A storm surge driven by hurricane force north-westerly winds whipped up the waters of the North Sea into massive tidal levels which then smashed through sea wall fortifications, breaching more than 1,200 sites. Whole communities were isolated, 32,000 people had to be evacuated from their homes, 1,000 miles of coastline was flooded and 307 people lost their lives.

For the people of Essex, it was the greatest tragedy in the county's history. The disaster struck with a hideous force and more than 49,000 acres were flooded, including the greater part of the coastal fringe. There were 113 deaths in the county and 13,000 people were driven from their homes. Thousands were evacuated from Canvey Island, hundreds moved from Tilbury and Purfleet. All the islands on the north bank of the Thames estuary were inundated — and a month later were still under water.

It began on Friday 30th January, 1953, when a deep depression moved from Iceland in a south-easterly direction and gale force winds struck the north coast of Scotland late that night. Next morning the average wind speed at the Orkneys was 90 mph with gusts up to 125 mph. The gale forced a tremendous volume of Atlantic water, estimated at more than four billion cubic yards, southwards into the North Sea. This coincided with a spring tide and raised the sea 10 feet above normal.

The first indication of the disaster to come occurred at Aberdeen in the early hours of Saturday morning when the sea rose about 2.5 feet above the predicted level. The great tide then rolled south into the ever-increasing bottleneck of the North Sea — and the water rose higher and higher. At 3.30 pm the River Tees began to overflow its banks and, at 5.25 the sea broke through the sandhills on the Lincolnshire coast.

At 7.10pm water began to pour into the town centre of Mablethorpe and 6,000 people had to be evacuated from the coastal strip between Mablethorpe and Sutton-on-Sea; 16 were drowned and 20 more perished in the area near Skegness. Thirty minutes later, the sea defences on the north coast of Norfolk were overwhelmed. Fifteen people were drowned at King's Lynn and a further 65 between King's Lynn and Hunstanton. The sea walls at Yarmouth were breached, 10 people lost their lives, 35,000 homes in the Southtown district were flooded and there was extensive evacuation. The great tide, still not at its highest point, rolled south towards Essex.

The inhabitants of the east coast had spent the Saturday afternoon going about their usual tasks. There were certainly heavy winds and high tides but on this late January day this was not unusual and there was little anxiety. Many of the residents of Canvey Island had attended a public ceremony dedicating a new memorial hall to the memory of the local men killed in the war. On the mainland opposite Canvey, the finishing touches were being applied to the new Benfleet secondary school due to be officially opened on Monday. At the sailing clubs of Harwich, Dovercourt and right down the Essex coast, enthusiasts were carrying out repairs and renovations to their boats. All day the wind was blowing but it never attained anything like the velocities experienced in the north.

On Saturday evening, normal activities continued. Ambulance competitions were held at the railway club at Parkeston Quay. Outside the winds howled and the after-dinner speakers had to compete with the roar of the gale. On Southend Pier and at the new memorial hall on Canvey Island, dances were in progress. People were enjoying themselves at the theatre in Clacton, the Savoy Cinema at Sutton-on-Sea and a few hardy people took an evening stroll to experience the freshness of the wind and to observe the lashing seas.

Those indoors listening to the wireless were more concerned about the terrible shipping accident in the Irish Sea in the early hours of Saturday morning. The British Railways Ferry, *MV Princess Victoria* (2,694 tons) crossing from Stranraer to Larne had run into the hurricane-force gale and listed so badly that the captain had given orders to abandon the ship. Men had formed a human chain to get women and children out of the lounge and into the lifeboats before she foundered, capsized and sank.

The news bulletins described how lifeboats had rushed to her aid into the teeth of the gale and picked up 44 survivors. But it was feared, and later confirmed, that the rest of the 176 passengers and crew on board *MV Princess Victoria* had perished in the mountainous seas. It was the greatest disaster suffered by any British Merchant vessel in peacetime for a quarter of a century, but the significance of what had happened, in relation to the perilous position in which the population of the low lying East coast of England was now placed, was not yet apparent.

It was not until 9.10 pm that conditions became disturbing. It was reported from Southend pier head that the tide was early and rising fast. The Harwich harbour master noticed that the tide, with three and a half hours still to flow, had reached its predicted high water level. A message was dispatched from Harwich to Clacton police station: "Water will be over quay here when high tide occurs at 1 am. Southend

A rowing boat negotiates the flooded main street of Harwich, looking for people in need of help. A quarter of the population of Harwich — about 3,500 — were homeless by Sunday, flooded out by 12 feet of water when the Bathside sea wall collapsed. It was during that first rush that several elderly people living in basements were engulfed without warning and perished. Heroes of the great evacuation that followed were the sailors of HMS Ganges and other ships who walked in the water until they were numb and exhausted, pushing boatloads of people along the main streets.

This aerial picture shows the break in the sea wall at Jaywick and the trail of mud and wreckage which the receding waters have left in their wake. Survivors who were taken to improvised rest centres in Clacton hotels and the Red Cross headquarters had harrowing experiences to relate to reporters of the East Essex Gazette. One of them, Mr Ted Bangle sat in a corner with his grandson, who asked — 'where is grannie?' "She has gone," Mr Bangle told the newspaper. "I heard the water crash against the wall of my house. I struggled to the door carrying Terry and with my wife Helen at my side. As we opened the door my wife was swept off her feet and carried away. I haven't seen her since."

and London get high tide two hours later and the Thames will no doubt flood with the high wind."

The warning went down the line — to the county police divisions at Colchester, Chelmsford, Braintree, Brentwood and Grays, to the county borough of Southend, to the sub divisions and to London. Police stations with the most vulnerable waterfronts to supervise were advised to pass the warning on to the owners of premises which were likely to flood. It was a routine alarm. By 10 pm the progress of the tide was being watched by the county police, by the harbourmaster at Harwich, by the Essex River Board's sluice-keeper at Holland Haven and by the duty officer on Southend pier. As the gale persisted,

trees blew down at Kirby Cross and Wakering. All the time the tide was rising steadily and the pent up energy of the North Sea was thrusting against sea walls, softening up mile upon mile of the defences and undermining the subsoil. Yet the majority of the people of the Essex coastal towns and villages, now asleep in their beds, had no idea of the disaster that was about to strike.

Harwich was the first town in Essex to "go under". Built on a small peninsula jutting out into the Stour Estuary, it was attacked simultaneously from three sides and, by midnight, the quay, the esplanade and the Bathside area were flooded. Minutes later the pier was submerged and the water surged into the

East Essex Gazette, February 6, 1953.   REGISTERED AT THE G.P.O. AS A NEWSPAPER.

East Essex Gazette

CLACTON TIMES · FRINTON & WALTON TIMES · BRIGHTLINGSEA TIMES

No. 1954   FRIDAY, FEBRUARY 6, 1953   PRICE THREEPENCE

Troops move into stricken area for road-by-road clean-up

BATTERED JAYWICK IS NOW SEALED OFF

Little can be done until flood waters subside

TODAY the battered holiday township of Jaywick lies sealed off from the world and has all the appearances of a deserted film set—a set against which the greatest tragedy that has ever befallen North-East Essex has been played.

Police guard every entrance. Troops are ready to seal off the township still further with barbed-wire. Everyone is waiting—waiting for the floods to subside. Until that happens little can be done.

As soon as the water falls a carefully organised recovery plan will swing into action. Troops will move in to start a road-by-road clean-up. Gas and electrical engineers will begin re-piping and re-wiring.

To-day 120 airmen, 300 soldiers and 20 men from Clacton Council's surveyor's department are employed on the release of the 2,000 million gallons of sea water which swamped Jaywick in a sea of death. But when the roar of the Army amphibious craft dies down for a moment the whirring of the police motor boats can still be heard as the search for victims who may still be entombed in their homes goes on.

37 DEAD

UP to last night 37 dead had been recovered from the floods. Thirty-five were from Jaywick and two from Point Clear. It is feared that more bodies may be recovered as the floods go down.

The recovered dead are:

JESSIE FRENCH (77), 14, Beach-crescent.
NELLIE BURNETT (87), 87, Meadow-way.
LILLIAN CROSSWELL

Officials of all authorities concerned in the rehabilitation of flood-stricken areas have already made arrangements for the military to move in with proper recovery equipment.

The cause of the flood is expected to be the subject of a national inquiry, but it is generally accepted that the sea defences at Jaywick proved sound. They withstood the onslaught of the sea with only minor breaches. The tragedy occurred when a torrent of water swamped her from her poorly protected right flank.

CLERK'S STATEMENT
In a statement made yesterday,

Two pictures which illustrate the devastating nature of the week-end's floods at Jaywick.   ABOVE: The receding waters have left a trail of mud and wreckage, with bungalows at   crazy angles. BELOW: The heart of Jaywick after the water had started to subside.

ON OTHER PAGES

February 6th, 1953 — and the front page of the East Essex Gazette.

town centre, down streets and into basements. Great waves rolled in and out of gardens, lashed against shops and houses and presented Harwich with a scene of unbelievable chaos. The whole of the town, from the quay to the police station was under several feet of water, which carried with it garden fences, gates, rubbish and even furniture.

Inevitably there was tragedy. At The Anchor public house the landlord and his wife were trying to rescue some barrels of beer when the water rushed in. The landlord's wife escaped but he was trapped when the rush of water slammed the cellar door shut. Rescuers cut through the floor of the bar to reach his body. Seven other people drowned including a mother and baby and the man who was trying to save them. More than 3,000 Harwich people were homeless.

The railway embankment at Parkeston Quay was breached at both ends and more than half a mile of track was washed away. By one am, the electricity had failed and Harwich was in the dark. The tide had not yet started to ebb.

Farther south towards Dovercourt and Walton, beach huts were swallowed up by the waves and

sent floating out to sea. The tide advanced up the estuaries of the Stour, Colne, Blackwater and Crouch. Acres of farmland were engulfed, boats were torn from their moorings and those on higher ground, bordering the Dengie Peninsula found themselves encircled by the sea. And still it was rising.

At Walton, the police were warning people to evacuate the danger area where water was coming over the Esplanade. Already furniture in bungalows and ground floors was floating but, at 12.30 am the police car operating in the area radioed to Clacton. "All persons warned of danger to life. Everything here under control."

There was nothing under control at Jaywick. The little holiday resort with 1,700 chalet bungalows was in a state of complete turmoil. By 1.45 on the Sunday morning there were 22 breaches in the sea wall fronting the north bank of the Colne Estuary and millions of gallons of water were being channelled across St Osyth marshes towards the back of Jaywick to meet the water coming in from the sea. Within minutes the village was swamped with a 2,000 million gallon torrent, driven by the violent wind and

(continued on P68)

Volunteers were quick to come forward during and in the period immediately after the floods and were quietly and efficiently supervised by the Essex police who coped with a great variety of tasks. Here a small, but grateful, Canvey Island resident is carried to safety.

During the night, frogmen from HMS Mars attempted to raise the manhole covers to allow the water to get away from the main street in Harwich. Many of the town's flood victims were trapped in the basements of houses and the police opened up the Harwich boating pool and released its dinghies. One man was seen rowing a dinghy with cats at the stern, dogs in the middle and a parrot.

reinforced by 30 more breaches along the St Osyth beach. The current stripped the grass off the land as it passed over it and caravans were smashed to pieces. When it reached Jaywick it rose so fast that people were drowned in their beds. Survivors clambered onto wardrobes, tables, lofts and rooftops as the water continued to rise.

The *East Essex Gazette* reported the tragedy: "Within minutes of the crushing, brutal wave of death a complete rescue service was being organised. Police, firemen, ambulance workers toiled ceaselessly beside Clacton councillors, Boy Scouts and ordinary men and women. Boatmen sweated in the freezing air and hundreds worked to help the inhabitants. Little boats carried the survivors to safety through the streets and past a noticeboard which read 'To the sea' but the sea has come to meet it".

Thirty five people were drowned in Jaywick on that February morning and two more bodies were recovered from the flooded stores at Point Clear Bay. The last person to come out of the village alive was a 65-year-old nursing sister, Louise Kemp who was trapped in her loft for 31 hours.

The *Gazette* wrote: "But for her tabby cat, Tiger, she might have died. As the water rose to the height of her bed he pawed her. She awoke, clambered onto a wardrobe, but still the water rose. She then took a clothes hanger from the back of the cupboard and smashed her way through the ceiling of her bedroom into the loft. There she stayed, wrapped in a cotton nightdress and sodden wet blanket, foodless, lightless and shivering. Rescuers, searching for survivors, eventually saw her distress signal made out of a strip of blanket".

At Colne Point one family were just going to bed when they saw the tide flowing over the sea wall. The bungalow was surrounded by the sea and two of their three boats had floated away. The family — a man, his wife, two fishermen sons and a daughter who was sick — decided to take the third boat and row for safety across the marshes, with the girl's pony swimming astern. Into the wind and across the waves they rowed. One son fell overboard but they managed to pull him back. Before their eyes they saw an enormous wave break over the sea wall and crash into 20 wood and concrete bungalows. They completely disintegrated. For two hours the family battled on until they reached dry land at Lee Wick.

An elderly couple who lived behind their grocer's stores in Point Clear Bay, on the other side of the bay from Brightlingsea, received a telephone call from their son who lived in a cafe some 300 yards away a little way up Beacon Hill. The son had tried to reach them but the height and force of the waves was too great. He told his parents to wade through to the two-storey house next door and go upstairs. His father said the shop was awash. Then he said: "The windows are coming in." The mother then spoke to her son. "Save yourself, I'm drowning," she said. The telephone went dead.

The tidal waters surged up the Colne Estuary, drowning sheep on the marshlands, rushing into

The signboard adds an ironic touch to this picture of refugees escaping the sea at Jaywick. In places it was flooded to a depth of 3.5 metres (12 feet).

the town centre of Brightlingsea and reaching Wivenhoe and Colchester Hythe. Wivenhoe is built on a hill which rises from the quay but the seafaring residents on the quayside took to their bedrooms and watched, in the moonlight, a tremendous volume of water swamp the boatyard. The residents of Toll-gate House were isolated with water up to the kitchen ceiling and the house in danger of collapse. On the other side of the river, houses in the High Street at Rowhedge were two or three feet deep in water — not from the collapse of the river walls but the volume of water which flowed over the top.

On the west side of the Hythe, water coming over the quayside and towpath raced into the gasworks and put out the boiler fires. By 2 am water was pouring into the electricity generating station and both gas and electricity supplies to Colchester were out of action. As the night wore on the flooding grew worse. Waves overwhelmed the land on either side of the Blackwater. They flowed down the Goldhanger-Heybridge Road, tipping over caravans and even washing one of them up on top of the sea wall. In Maldon, the canal and river united to become a vast unbroken sheet of water swamping the golf course and, on the other side of the river, a couple returning from a party drove straight into the advancing tide.

The engine stalled. They removed the car seats on to the roof of the car and, still in evening dress, remained there while the angry waters of the Blackwater advanced around them.

Meanwhile, further south, the defences on the Dengie Peninsula between the Blackwater and the Crouch were unable to cope with the force of the tide or the volume of water which was pounding them. The river board man at St Peter's at the north of the peninsula heard a sound "like a clap of thunder," saw the walls "let go" and watched the sea "burst into the fields in a seething cauldron of froth and bubble". For miles and miles along the marshes, the defences simultaneously gave way and the floods spread and deepened until they formed a massive sea lake.

On the north bank of the Crouch there were two major breaches at Burnham and water flowed down the High Street, through the gardens and into the adjacent streets. By 1pm all buildings between the quay and town centre were flooded and the tide was still rising. On the south bank, where the creeks of the Crouch cut between the islands of Wallasea, Foulness, Havengore, Potton, Rushley and New England, events were taking a critical turn.

At Wallasea the occupants of bungalows near the Creeksea Ferry Inn joined hands and battled through

(continued on P74)

The bungalow beach settlement of Jaywick. Most of the 1,800 chalets were used only in the summer, but about 250 were occupied that night. mainly by retired folk. There was no precise knowledge of which chalets were occupied and which empty and, as there were no lights, the rescuers did not know where to call. Many people had to smash their way into the roof space through the ceiling, but the water still managed to lift many chalets off their footings and toss them around like matchwood. The average age of the 37 people who died at Jaywick was 66.

It was at Jaywick where some of the most terrifying scenes in north Essex were witnessed. One crippled lady, 42-year-old Miss Marie Miles, telephoned friends from her bungalow home which lay directly in the path of the flood. She warned Mr and Mrs Reeves of Rosemary Way of the approaching danger and the couple and their children just managed to crowd into their tiny loft as floodwater, eight feet deep, poured into their bungalow. The next day they found Miss Miles had died. Paralysed from the waist down and unable to escape, she was drowned when the icy water surged into her home.

It was several days before the police and volunteer helpers recovered all the bodies from Jaywick. Onlookers stood with bowed heads as the boats returned from their grim mission, down the submerged avenues and lifted the bodies, draped in grey blankets onto the waiting ambulances.

Two men. Mr R.E. Fawcett of Clacton and his neighbour Mr C.H.Marsh found a canvas canoe and set off in the direction of shouts for help. In high winds and a strong current they had great difficulty in managing the craft but they eventually reached a house where the cries were hysterical. "There we found the occupants, with no attic for refuge, standing in water up to their waists — a grandmother, her son and his two daughters aged nine and 13. We got the children into the canoe, landed them safely and returned for the adults. A few doors away we smashed a window and saw an elderly couple both dead. We passed several other houses where there was silence from within."

Below: Unusual transport in the main road at Harwich.

No lives were lost at Walton-on-the-Naze but a total of 194 dwellings were inundated causing distress to 525 people. A few elderly folk died later in hospital of shock

FINAL NIGHT EXTRA

Jacqmar
Ready-to-Wear
16 Grosvenor Street W.1

Evening Standard
40,040   MONDAY, FEBRUARY 2, 1953   Three-halfpence

Holland Toffee
Best on Earth
SOUTHPORT LANCS.

100 BODIES FOUND ON CANVEY ISLAND

And this was the scene there to-day

23 women & children missing in plane

Evening Standard Reporter

Ten British servicemen, their wives and 13 children, are in an airliner missing over the North Atlantic since early to-day.

The airliner, a four-engined York, with a crew of six, was taking the 33 passengers from Britain to Jamaica. It is owned by Skyways, of London, and is on charter to the War Office for flying troops and their families.

The front page of the Evening Standard on the day after the disaster.

73

Wallasea, where the sea and the River Crouch merged, and people were trapped in their homes.

a swift current some five feet deep to farm buildings. They spent the rest of the night in a hayloft. The licensee of the inn and her three customers also tried to make a dash for safety but the car was up to the bonnet in water and wouldn't start. They went back to the inn and two men climbed onto the roof. The licensee, who decided to fetch a coat from her bedroom, and a customer, who held a torch for her, were too late and found their way blocked by a great wall of water. They climbed on to a table but this was swept from under their feet and they were left hanging from the top of a door, with one foot of air space between them and the ceiling. It was 5 am before rescuers arrived in a boat. The two men were

still on the roof but the third, unable to hang on, had drowned. The landlady, Mrs Ivy Taylor-Smith, was alive. The rescuers saw her, in a black frock, hanging over the top of the door, with one foot supporting her weight on the door handle.

She later told the *Evening Echo:* "Charles Rolfe, who was hanging on the door with me said he was going to swim for help. The last I saw of him he was swimming away with the torch in his hand. He drowned and the police found him still clutching his torch. The water continued to rise, until I could only just hold my head above it. Luckily the pressure of the air in the room kept the water line steady after it reached my neck. There were things floating about

The rescue operation continued at Foulness and the picture shows an old man being pulled to safety in a cart with his dog. Not everyone was so lucky — the Army recovered the bodies of two women, one on Tuesday 3rd February and the other not until Saturday 14th. Two people from the island died in hospital. Mr Jerry Driscoll, aged 40 and his 84-year-old mother Ellen — both from exposure and pneumonia.

my head and there were times when I thought the ordeal was never going to end and perhaps I had better let go and die. I was rescued just before dawn by a farmer, Col Carey who somehow managed to get me out through the kitchen window."

The other fatality at Wallasea Island was that of an auxiliary postman. His body was not recovered until March 8, when it was found in a ditch behind the sea wall. How many people had perished on Foulness Island no-one knew. By 2 am the only road connecting it to the mainland was under water and access by boat was impossible due to the wind and heavy seas. Foulness had become one great expanse of water which stretched as far as the eye could see, with a few trees visible above the water line. It was not until 9 o'clock on Sunday evening that the Southend Lifeboat managed to reach the island where they discovered hundreds of people stranded in upstairs rooms but reluctant to leave their homes until daybreak. A message, on the midnight news, was broadcast by the BBC to the people of Foulness telling them that another attempt would be made on Monday morning.

Police also flashed a message to county control. "It is proposed to try and get to Foulness Island at

(continued on P78)

ABOVE: These 34 Nissen huts stood on six acres of land at Great Wakering and were occupied by young couples who had been given temporary accommodation by Rochford council. An enormous breach in the sea wall at Morrins Point allowed sea water to rush in at violent speed and engulf the housing estate. Some residents were able to snatch a few belongings and wade down the lane, at first knee deep, then waist deep carrying their children. Others were afraid to wade as the current grew stronger and, still in their night clothes, broke through the corrugated roofs and clung on with absolutely no protection from the powerful icy gusts which threatened to hurl them in the waves. In these harrowing conditions they waited for up to nine hours to be rescued. Six people drowned.

RIGHT: Thousands of people were evacuated from Canvey Island — some by bus and some by boats. Others, like the old couple here, preferred to hitch up their dress, roll up the trouser leg and make their own way to safety. One of the heroes of the Canvey evacuation was Reg Stevens, then council engineer and one of the key men involved in the flood operations. He told the Evening Echo that there was a shortage of boats, so he broke into a small factory which made canvas dinghies; these were soon put to good use. He said: "It was chaotic but by and large there was no great panic. There were people on the roofs waiting to be rescued and I remember one poor old lady spreadeagled on a tree".

When this picture was taken, the great Tilbury evacuation was underway. Already more than 5,000 people had been rescued, half the population of the town. At one stage it was feared that every resident would have to be moved because of a breakdown in the town's sewage system. These people were being taken from their flooded homes in Civic Square while others waited on the roof terrace for their turn.

0600 hours tomorrow (Monday). There are between 300 and 400 people there. Will you please alert medical services as we are doubtful as to the conditions we are likely to find there. Also there are a number of boats leaving from Burnham to try and effect a landing. Would it be possible for some medical services to be laid on to travel by these boats?"

None of the rescue crews which left for Foulness at daybreak on Monday had any idea what lay ahead on the island, which had been cut off from relief for 30 hours. They found sheep drowned, some entangled in fences. They found pheasants and partridges taking refuge in trees. They found rabbits floating, alive, on pieces of timber and even up trees. And they found two victims, drowned.

There was more drama and even greater tragedy at Great Wakering, a small village just four miles north of Southend and, ironically, one of the driest villages in England in terms of rainfall. Just after 1am, water began to flow into a temporary housing estate of 34 Nissen huts, sited in a hollow in the middle of Great Wakering Common. The 37 families (112 people) awoke to find the sea forcing its way under their doors. Some made a bid to escape, wading waist-deep out of the estate carrying their

The lovely old church of St Mary's at Foulness, completely surrounded by calm, tranquil waters, looks peaceful enough. But this was taken on the cold, bright morning of Sunday 1st February — the morning after the night before — when 200 people managed to escape from the uncontrollable rage of the North Sea, and two people perished.

children. But the flood grew deeper and the current stronger and the remainder clambered out of their windows on to the corrugated roofs, clinging on precariously and dressed only in their night clothes. One elderly couple couldn't reach the roof so they climbed onto their stove, where they remained for nine hours, up to their chests in water. Another elderly couple drowned in their Nissen hut and so did a young mother and her child. Two others, a man and a child, died later in hospital from shock and exposure.

Wakering firemen had been alerted but, when they reached the lane leading to the common, the water was so deep the appliance couldn't go any further. Hero of the hour was a local brickfield worker who found a flat bottom boat large enough to carry himself, one adult and one child. He reached the huts which were almost submerged, with just the corrugated roofs projecting above the surface, and began to ferry the survivors to and fro. Alone,

he saved 30 people before other, bigger boats joined in, the crews having great difficulty with the rough seas and the wind which often drove them past the hut they were making for.

At Southend Pier, the automatic recorder which measures the height of the tide, went out of action three feet above the danger level. By this time most of the Marine Parade was under water and within a few minutes the sea had engulfed the Western Esplanade, The Leas, Chalkwell Gardens and the Sunken Gardens. The Southend works of the North Thames Gas Board was inundated, 600 homes were flooded and acres of glasshouses smashed. There were outbreaks of fire as a result of electrical "shorting" but the fire brigade crews could not drive their appliances through the water. It didn't matter — the fires were put out by the tide. There were two fatalities in Southend. One man stepped out of bed into water and died of shock and another man, who was trapped for some time, died later of pneumonia.

The evacuation of Canvey Island was completed on Monday afternoon, 2nd February but, at that stage, the number of missing was not known and rumour placed the death toll at several hundred. With such an element of doubt it was decided to comb the island, road by road, house by house, looking on roofs, in

Men of the Royal Air Force at work on Canvey Island, sealing one of the 40 gaps torn in the sea defences,

attics and roof spaces for those who might have perished. The long line of bedraggled survivors in the photograph presented one vital question — will we see such pictures again, or will the sea defences become a national responsibility?

with sandbags. The majority did not return home until after the spring tides on 19th February.

The uncertainty about the number of people who had perished on Canvey Island became a matter of national anxiety. The caption to this picture, taken on 2nd February, indicated that the Canvey toll was already rising towards 100 and 400 were still missing.

By midnight, the sea was already in the cockle sheds at Leigh-on-Sea and minutes later was pouring into the railway station. At 1 am the local electricity supply failed. On Two Tree Island, off Leigh, a distress message was received by Southend police from the two operators of the sewage works. Then the telephone failed and the men were cut off from all communication with the mainland. They were found the next day by Leigh fishermen, marooned on the roof of the works.

The tidal surge hit Canvey Island like a battering ram and nowhere on the whole east coast was more devastating or tragic; in fact the full horror of what happened in the early hours of Sunday 1st February 1953 still casts a shadow over the island today. All inhabitants found themselves fighting for their lives as a surging icy torrent engulfed the island like a violent nightmare. A few had been warned and took refuge in attics and lofts. For others, the margin between life and death was a matter of seconds as

the Tewkes Creek Wall collapsed just after 1 am and the sea burst through into the area of Canvey known as Sunken Marsh.

In her book *The Great Tide,* Hilda Grieve describes those moments. "Families were awakened by the sudden roar as the wall burst, by the swish of the water as it rushed past, by the clatter and crash of debris striking the house, by the noise of the splitting timber and splintering glass. Half awake, dazed and bewildered, as they struggled to escape, to reach the outdoor staircases to their lofts, or to fight their way through the tumult outside or to go to the aid of elderly relatives and neighbours, successive waves, charging through the walls, swept them off their feet. Many who clambered on chairs, tables, cookers, mangle-tables and step ladders, to keep their heads above the water, or to make holes in the flimsy ceilings in order to escape into the roof space, found their supports swept away from under their feet, leaving them fighting in the dark with floating

An ambulanceman carries a Canvey woman to safety while a soldier follows with the few possessions she was allowed to bring with her.

furniture, clutching desperately at fanlights or the tops of doors and wardrobes and trying to hold children above the suffocating water. The Sunken Marsh was well described as a 'basin of death'.

Within 15 minutes the water was above window sill level, sweeping towards the High Street and joining up with other areas already flooded. The current became so swift that one man described a shed floating by as "travelling as fast as a bus". The tragedy of the next hour — as the watery avalanche completely engulfed Canvey Island, carrying caravans, sheds, furniture, timber, water tanks and bodies — and the heroism and resourcefulness that followed, can never be adequately recorded. Many people were drowned in their beds and others died of shock or exposure as they clambered onto roofs and waited, shivering in the dark, for help.

The tragedy and gallantry of some must speak for all. Mr Charles Stevens and his wife Elsie scrambled on top of a wardrobe, found the strength to punch a hole in the ceiling, dragged the children onto the roof and waited 11 hours to be rescued. A young woman with her husband and two children were awakened by the sound of their baby crying. They found her cot floating. The mother, a good swimmer, climbed out out of the window and swam to the Central Wall Road with the idea of fetching help. Half way across she realised she could not go any further against the strong current and swam back. When she reached the bungalow, she clambered into the attic, found some bedding and blankets and tore them into strips to make a rope. Leaning out of the attic window she threw the makeshift rope down to her husband, a non-swimmer, who was sitting on the windowsill below with the children. One by one she hauled them up to safety.

With more than six square miles being engulfed and more than 11,000 people in imminent danger, somebody had to take the initiative and organise the

(continued on P86)

A rescue worker, up to his thighs in flood water comes across an isolated house on Canvey Island and calls — "is there anyone in there ?" For several days the grim search for both survivors and victims continued. The task was co-ordinated by the police. By Saturday night, 7th February, 607 people had been discovered. They had remained on the island.

As the floods recede another survivor of Canvey is found and lowered gently into the rescue boat

island's rescue operation. The Canvey Island surveyor called the fire brigade, a retained station which adjoined the council offices. Eight part-time firemen turned up within minutes and drove their appliance through the water to the High Street. They could go no further, so they sounded the siren, fired maroons as a warning, plunged into the water chest deep and waded towards the cries for help.

The firemen were joined by a few other able bodied people who had escaped in time including a policeman and a Roman Catholic priest. From the roads around the High Street they helped women and children down from ceiling rafters and wardrobes and rescued a couple who were clinging to an iron bedstead. All the time the water was rising rapidly but, until boats could be found, rescue work north of the High Street was impossible.

Leigh Beck primary school and Long Road secondary school were opened as rest centres and the council surveyor rang the mainland to tell them that a major disaster was occurring on the island. He asked Chelmsford police headquarters for rescue vehicles, ambulances and reinforcements to be sent over as soon as water went down at the bridge across to Canvey (it remained impassable until 3 am). He emphasised that islanders must be evacuated. His call was just in time. Minutes later, telephonic communication with the mainland broke down.

The plight of the people who were trapped was terrible. For many hours they clung on to doors or floating furniture, their bodies numb in the icy water. Many collapsed and slipped into the water to suffer an agonising end and others died of exposure. Some attempted to swim to safety, to no avail. The death toll on Canvey Island that Sunday morning was 58. Many others died in the days after the tragedy, their lives cut short by the extreme conditions they had endured.

Old and weak though he is, fate has dealt another blow to this elderly man wrapped in a quilt. He has lost his home at Canvey Island and now huddles, with another survivor, in Benfleet Methodist Church reception centre.

The cameraman's plane swoops low over an isolated house in the Thames Estuary as a boat reaches the front door. The men in the boat look up and the occupants wave. Another rescue operation is completed — but the search goes on.

To the west of Canvey, the newly improved sea wall protecting the great oil installations on the Corringham marshes at Shell Haven was overtopped and the old sea wall further on collapsed. The operators on duty in the crude distillation unit, which had gone into production for the first time that afternoon, closed down all units. The sites were abandoned as sea poured in through great gaps in the wall.

By 1.40 am water had risen around the Tilbury and Riverside General Hospital to a depth of four feet and patients were warned that they might have to be taken to the dock and evacuated by ship. It was not until the tide turned that Tilbury was really threatened. On ebb, the water which had flooded the lower part of the town from the dock tidal basin flowed back into the Thames and, within minutes, water in the streets was more than waist deep — and rising. Two police sergeants, six constables and some residents spent the rest of the night warning the people of Tilbury. They blew whistles and shouted. They banged on doors. They helped the old and infirm to escape. One boy saw his dog floating past on a large cake tray and an old lady of 79 was trapped by floodwater in a downstairs toilet and drowned.

Hardly a house in Tilbury escaped; in fact 2,500 houses out of 2,750 in the town became progressively flooded to a depth of five feet. 10,000 were forced to stay upstairs. The plant at the sewage works was submerged and in the early hours of the morning a public address police car broadcast a warning to the people of Tilbury not to flush their toilets.

Simultaneous disaster struck Purfleet and the Canning Town area of West Ham. Here the inflow of nearly 142 million gallons (640 million litres) of water converted 250 acres into a massive lake. In the middle were factories, shops, railways, commercial buildings, schools, churches and more than 1,100 houses. A nightwatchman who escaped drowning was killed by coal gas escaping from a fractured main.

Central London caught the tail end of the catastrophe. Water lapped the top of the parapet along the Victoria and Chelsea embankments and Millbank. The defences were overtopped by a few inches at Greenwich, Woolwich and London Bridge. In Kent, the southern shore of the Thames Estuary and the towns and villages from Woolwich to the North Foreland were heavily battered.

By Monday the disaster was a matter of intense personal anxiety to thousands of people all over the world. It was a national calamity, vividly reported by local and national press. The BBC correspondent who flew over the area said in his report: "One has to come low to see the devastation that is really there. Canvey Island — bits of furniture, belongings floating — and the absolute desolation of the scene, and the

Across the sea of floodwater between Leigh-on-Sea and Benfleet, three locomotives, locked together make their way to the station for help with relief work. Many other trains in the vicinity were marooned and many miles of railway track submerged.

waters still and sinister around the houses — and in those houses, what? People? Well, if so they were making no sign, and all around there were just the waters and no sign of movement. And then we came to Foulness — just the tops of farms, roofs of barns, and a herd of cattle wandering untended, splashing knee deep up a river that was once a road leading to a farm -— wandering up there for milking time — to a farm that isn't there any more. And a boat caught in a tree top, people struggling to get clear. And a heap of caravans thrown together in Jaywick, a deserted village...."

Gifts for the people of Essex poured in from all over the world. Furniture, bedding, fuel, clothes, sandbags, money, offers of accommodation, transport and machinery of all descriptions were freely given by manufacturers, individuals, tradesmen and community clubs in an unprecedented gesture of goodwill. Distribution centres for clothes, feeding centres and mobile homes were set up. There was Government help for farmers and urgent high level consultations on the need to reinstate tidal defences.

Before the mopping up had even begun, the 1953 tidal surge had earned a place in history as the most catastrophic weather event ever recorded in Britain. Those who lived through the nightmare have never forgotten it — and nor have we ever forgotten the indomitable spirit of those people of Harwich, Walton, Clacton, Jaywick, Mersea, Wallasea, Great Wakering, Foulness, Harwich, Tilbury, West Ham and hundreds of other communities big and small along the coastal fringe of Essex. Their resolution, courage and defiance was typified by a sign on Canvey Island which read: "Bear up, Canvey will rise again."

A photograph that speaks for itself. It was taken on Canvey Island on 2nd February, 1953.

How Canvey rose again

AND Canvey did rise again. The devastation of the 1953 floods provided the shock measures to get the community on its feet and, more importantly, to bring about an increase in the height and strength of the sea walls round the island. The North Sea, in 1953, made a mockery of the defences and the Waverley Committee, appointed to examine the disaster advocated research into the origins, behaviour and frequency of storm surges and the building of adequate defences to combat them.

Every urban and borough council along the coastal fringe of Essex also urged the need for the walls to be made safe and for Government money to be provided for what would be a multi-million pound task. The problem was tackled immediately and engineers worked at a tremendous speed, although it was to be many years before the defences were completed. Twenty years later it was considered that, of the 267 miles of defences maintained by the Essex River Division of the Anglian Water Authority, 225 miles could withstand a surge of the severity of 1953.

The red letter day for Canvey came on 25th February, 1983 when John Wakeham, MP for Rochford and Maldon unveiled a plaque on the walls of the great Benfleet flood barrier which was part of a £520 million scheme to protect Thameside areas and London from floods "for 1,000 years". The Canvey defences also include a barrier at Fobbing which is 120 feet wide and is held horizontally above spring tides and one at Easthaven which has three openings — two for the tide and one for boats using the creek. In London, which had teetered on the brink of a big disaster in 1953, the Thames Barrier was built at Woolwich for a cost of £450 million.

Meanwhile, in other parts of Essex, work continues on strengthening, consolidating and replacing walls so frequently damaged by the waves. Courage and resolution alone cannot keep the North Sea out for it will continue to strike with ungovernable rage and, at times, with the force of the tidal surge of 1953. Essex looks to the vigilance of the authorities and the skill of the engineers to keep it at bay.

There were plenty of royal visitors to Essex in February, 1953. They toured the stricken areas and gave encouragement to the flood victims. Queen Elizabeth II, still uncrowned, paid her first visit to Tilbury during those "drying days". She walked along the duckboards to houses at Tilbury's Poets Corner to take tea with some of those who had been rescued. Fresh cakes came out of cupboards that only days earlier had floated around Tilbury with the rest of the furniture. The Queen Mother, so recently widowed, was another visitor. Clearly moved by the sight of refugees, she went from one community to another talking to families who were still trying to salvage what they could of their belongings. She went into council houses that were once awash, where curtains, carpets, household linen were hanging from windows to dry. Never is the spirit of tolerance, understanding and caring more evident than in adversity. The Queen Mum added humour and warmth to a brave but beleaguered county.

The first week of February, 1954 was severe as a blizzard swept through the county. Most of the rivers in Essex were frozen, fish died, villages were cut off and traffic on the roads came to a standstill. Photograph shows pancake ice flows at Benfleet Creek, Canvey — close to where hundreds of men were repairing the sea walls. For them the conditions were appalling.

Snow-covered boats by The Parade at Burnham early in 1958. Some exceptionally heavy falls occurred along the Essex coast on 23rd January. Shoeburyness was buried under a layer of 23 inches and, on 25th January, the temperature at Writtle dropped to 18F (-8C). Four days later it reached 57F (14C) at East Ham, and 55F (13C) was measured at Writtle.

The junction of Station Road and Devonshire Road, Burnham-on-Crouch on 23rd January, 1958. It was one of the deepest coverings of snow ever known along the Essex coast.

A snowplough goes to work clearing deep snow on the Bradwell Road, near Southminster. The photograph was taken on 24th January, 1958 when much of Essex was under many inches of snow after a violent blizzard in the night.

Another heavy snowfall, a few weeks after the January blizzard, caused considerable chaos in many parts of Essex and Hertfordshire, especially in the areas around the swollen River Lea which burst its banks. Evacuation centres were set up and many families living in wooden bungalows on the Riverside Estate near the then shanty town of Roydon had to be rescued by boat. Photograph shows Mrs Taylor welcoming back her husband who had rowed off to get fresh food supplies.

A spectacular electrical storm which struck Sussex on the late afternoon of Friday 5th September, 1958, travelled through Kent and London and reached Essex after dark. It was accompanied by a wall of rain which caused flooding, landslides and signal breakdowns on the railways and turned streets into raging rivers. It was estimated that there were more than two and a half thousand flashes of lightning in just two hours.

Streets turned into rivers

5th September, 1958

ENORMOUS hail pummelling the earth, vivid blinding flashes of lightning and deafening peals of thunder. This was the storm as it began in Sussex in the early evening of 5th September, 1958. Slowly, inexorably it moved north-east leaving a trail of damage in its wake. Spawning a tornado, it cut a swathe of destruction through Horsham and Crawley and released hail the size of tennis balls. It burst upon Kent with tropical intensity and, at Knockholt, near Sevenoaks, a two-hour rainfall of 5.14 inches (131mm) was measured — the second heaviest fall on record. Homes were struck by lightning and oil tanks set ablaze on the Isle of Grain. With undiminished fury this self-perpetuating thunderstorm flung itself at Essex.

The south of the county took the brunt and none more so than at Wickford. A sultry afternoon with a temperature of 75 F (24C) was a prelude to a sticky evening with the whole southern sky ablaze with lightning. It was not long before sheets of rain turned the placid waters of the River Crouch into a raging torrent and a wall of floodwater, six feet deep, raced through Wickford. Bus passengers were trapped and cars totally submerged, to be rescued the following morning by a builder in an ex-army amphibious vehicle.

More than 100 people were rescued from the upper rooms of their houses. Young children were carried to safety by firemen and policemen in a flotilla of small boats. They were provided with food and bedding at the Salvation Army Hall while Wickford secondary school was also used as a rest centre. At the height of the storm, tables and chairs were floating down the High Street and floodwaters stretched for nearly a mile along it. In the early, grey light of dawn one man was seen swimming home with the milk.

Northwards, towards Chelmsford, there was no weakening of the elements. Some two and a half thousand flashes of lightning lit up the sky in less than two hours. More than three inches (80mm) of rain fell at West Hanningfield and 2.75 inches (70mm) in Chelmsford — over a month's rainfall. Floodwater was five feet deep as the rivers Can and Chelmer burst their banks and hundreds of families fled their homes.

Police used boats to ferry trapped people and their babies to safety from bedroom windows at Coval Lane and Prykes Drive. A wall of water swept through the grounds of Chelmsford Hospital and isolated it. Two wards were evacuated and 30 patients moved, some on stretcher trollies.

At one point Chelmsford was entirely cut off and so were three men in Central Park who managed to scramble onto the roof of a shed and remain there until the early hours when they were rescued by policemen in a boat. In a cottage in Broomfield Road, a baby asleep on a settee was snatched from danger just in time as water completely submerged the furniture. At Great Baddow, one family received a fright when a large refrigerator, washed from a nearby storehouse, was hurled by the racing waters against their cottage. It punctured the wall and sent hundreds of gallons gushing inside. The floods cut off 40 people at Sandon Bridge and they were forced to spend the night in the local school.

Elsewhere in Essex the light of dawn revealed a desolate countryside with huge stretches of open water covering fields and roads. Between Rayleigh and Basildon, cars, buses and lorries lay abandoned; a ragged stationary convoy. Police and firemen asked one boat builder from Billericay for every boat he had got so that families and stock could be rescued from flooded farms. At Pitsea, six people took refuge in the police station when their homes became inundated.

Farmers worked through the night using tractor headlights to identify animals that needed help. In the morning they found that newly-gathered crops were either ruined or completely washed away. At Mountnessing Farm, a herd of dairy cows became marooned on high ground and the farmer decided to leave them there until the waters subsided. To his surprise they turned up outside the farm, having swum the swollen river. One, however, died.

Rail lines were severed. A landslide hit the track between Pitsea and Laindon and engineers worked throughout the weekend to clear it. Another occurred between Pitsea and Stanford-le-Hope. Troops helped to rescue passengers marooned on trains between London and Chelmsford. At Gidea Park, 2,000 stranded passengers were picked up by lorries sent from Warley Barracks, the headquarters of the Essex Regiment.

The storm caused agricultural damage estimated at £1 million and an appeal was launched to aid those afflicted by the tragedy. On a lighter note, cellars became filled with clouds of bubbles at the Chelmsford Star Co-operative premises in Moulsham Street. This was caused by water mixing with thousands of packets of detergent.

Four people were trapped in the upper deck of this bus and remained there all night. The Evening Standard front page tells the story of Wickford's great storm of 5th September, 1958.

Wickford had never known a storm like the one on 5th September 1958. Sheets of rain turned the River Crouch into a raging torrent and a wall of floodwater raced six feet deep through the town centre. Cars were submerged, passengers trapped on buses and trains and many rescued from their homes in boats. This picture was taken in Wickford as the water subsided.

At one stage Chelmsford was entirely cut off as the rivers Can and Chelmer burst their banks, causing hundreds of families to flee their homes. This aerial photograph was taken on 6th September, 1958 — the day after the great storm.

SOME years after the smog of 1952 which caused so many deaths, the people of Essex, and East Enders in particular, continued to experience more great "peasoupers". Photograph shows the conditions outside Liverpool Street station on the morning of 29th January, 1959 as traffic inches its way cautiously through the choking blanket and pedestrians wonder if its safe to cross the road. Road and rail traffic was affected by the worst fog of the winter and commuters from Essex were many hours' late to their offices. It wasn't unusual. Most years provided conditions that caused death and illness and some people made use of a special mask which purified the air before intake into the lungs. The fog also caused many accidents on road and railway but the greatest disaster was at Lewisham on 4th December, 1957 when two trains crashed in thick fog under a bridge which then collapsed onto the wrecked coaches. Ninety two passengers died and more than 200 were injured.

The summer of 1959 was one of the sunniest of the century and no more so than here at Point Clear, St Osyth, which has the added advantage of being one of the driest spots in the whole of Great Britain. The peak of the heatwave occurred in early July when the temperature soared into the nineties at Stansted. By 11th September it was still hot and on that day a reading of 85F (29C) was reached at Earls Colne. Point Clear Bay on this summer's day seems a long way from the tragedy it experienced in 1953.

CHAPTER NINE 1960 — 1969

A few legendary winters

1960: In a "Which" report published by the Consumers' Association in June of this year, 64 British holiday resorts were evaluated for their weather conditions. Averages of rainfall, sunshine and temperature were used during the past summer months and Southend scored consistently well — fourth for June, second for July and the winner for its weather in August. For September it was third. However, the summer of 1960 was not impressive. The highest temperature attained at Walton-on-the Naze was only 74F (23C).

1961: A burst of almost summery heat warmed many hearts on Valentine's Day (14th February), when the temperature reached 63F (17C). March was unusually dry and only 0.06 inches (1.2mm) fell at Coryton. On both the nights of 28th and 29th May, damaging frosts occurred at Writtle.

1962: In what was the coldest year since 1919, Essex at least boasted the warmest temperature in England with 82F (27.8C) on 3rd September at Writtle. The year began and ended under deep snow. On 1st January the mercury plunged to 13F (-10C) at Stansted. However, it quickly became much milder and stormy. Shoeburyness recorded a gust of 87 mph at 8.45 am on 11th January. Christmas was the coldest since 1897 and snow fell on Boxing Day — the start of a long cold winter when most of the county was under a white, icy blanket until early March, 1963.

1963: The winter 1962-3 was the coldest since 1740 and at Stanstead Abbots on the Essex-Herts border, a numbing minus 5F (-21C) was recorded on 23rd January, the coldest place in England that year. The bitter cold was exacerbated on the 19th January when winds of nearly 80 mph lashed the coast around Shoeburyness. This strength of wind gave a wind-chill equivalent temperature of -53F; frost bite was a real hazard for those venturing outside.

1964: The winter 1963-4 was extremely dry. Over England and Wales as a whole it was estimated to be the driest for 250 years. Dovercourt measured only 2.3 inches (59mm) of rainfall in three months. In a modest summer, the temperature did soar briefly to 89F (32C) at Earls Colne on 26th August.

1965: A vigorous depression moved south over England on 4th March bringing strong winds, heavy snow and chaos to Essex. The Chelmsford office of the AA received 200 weather-related calls and 50 pleas for assistance from motorists. Accidents were reported every few minutes and one lorry driver from Plaistow had a narrow escape when he was freed from his crushed lorry cab at Margaretting. The temperature had fallen on 3rd March to 16F (-9C) yet by the 29th there was a burst of summer weather, Harlow recording a very warm 73F (23C). For a while conditions were so dry that Chelmsford imposed a ban on the use of hosepipes.

1966: A sharp, cold spell in mid-January brought temperatures down to 14F (-10C) at Writtle. In April, spring came early with eight hours of sun on the 9th and the thermometer hovering at 61F (16C). A few days later, biting east winds swept across Essex and brought several inches of snow.

1967: Overall, across England, May was the wettest since 1729. Rainfall amounted to 3.52 inches (90mm) at Harlow and, at Stansted, thunder was heard on nine successive days. The month actually began with arctic air sweeping south and snow fell on several days. At night the temperature was just 27F (-3C).

1968: An infamous year due to the weekend deluge of rain in September which turned Essex rivers into fast-flowing torrents. January began with deep low pressure moving south-east across Devon and Cornwall which brought snow to Essex. Ponds, rivers and lakes were frozen and on Saturday 13th January, skaters enjoyed many hours of fun on Danbury Park Lakes. The thaw, when it came, was rapid and the skaters at Danbury were replaced, 48 hours later, by anglers in shirt-sleeves.

1969: Snow lay for more than 15 days at Earls Colne in February and the temperature fell to 12F (-11C) on the 8th. A blizzard on Friday night 7th February led to abandoned cars littering the roads and the AA dealing with more than 1,000 calls for help. Hundreds of motorists spent the weekend collecting their abandoned vehicles from Essex roads. In Halstead, a lorry skidded on the road outside The Bull public house and demolished part of the bridge across the river. October was unusually warm and dry — rainfall being the lowest since 1781 but equalled in 1947.

Happy New Year. A fairyland setting for the few passengers who took the double-decker bus ride along the A11 through Epping Forest on 1st January, 1962. On this wintry morning the temperature in many parts of Essex was just 13F (-10C). It quickly became milder and the snow cleared but it returned with a vengeance later in the year....

Sea freezes for seven miles

Winter of 1962-1963

IT started on Boxing Day, and for two icy months, Essex suffered the conditions of a bleak, cheerless Arctic environment. The winter of 1963-3 went down in the record books as the coldest since 1740. Along the Essex coastline the sea froze, rivers were jammed with ice floes and roads were snowbound. Unemployment figures were the worst since 1947. Not until 2nd March did the soil and the flattened grass show through the carpet of snow which had covered the county for the best part of 10 weeks.

The remarkable cold spell set in on 23rd December, 1962. On this day a cold airstream from central Russia spread to most parts of the UK. Even though it was sunny, the 23rd and 24th were exceptionally chilly in Essex and further north, in Scotland, a band of rain moved south, turning rapidly to snow.

It began to snow in Essex on Boxing Day afternoon and continued for 24 hours until a blanket, many inches deep in places, lay across the county. Already London had shivered through its coldest Christmas period since 1897 and there was worse to come. On Saturday 29th December, a blizzard raged in the southern counties and, whipped up by gale-force winds, the snow blew into drifts several feet deep. Nationwide, 200 roads and 95,000 miles of highway were snowbound.

The *Burnham-on-Crouch Advertiser* reported that "whatever chaos the conditions have brought, they have been welcomed by the holidaymaking youngsters who have revelled in the snow". The newspaper noted the absence of skaters on ponds and lakes and mourned the passing of those by-gone days when skating was the norm in frosty weather.

In the Dengie Hundred, many cars were completely buried in snowdrifts and, in some parts of Essex, the snow lay 12 inches deep, even where it had not piled up. On Saturday 30th December, the tide at Burnham lifted huge masses of snow and ice off the saltings which gave the rivers a truly Arctic appearance as they floated down on the tide.

Fleets of bulldozers, snowploughs and lorries were engaged by Essex County Council's Highways Department in a bid to keep roads open. Although the snow eased generally, the frost continued. The average afternoon temperature at Stansted was just 31F (-1C) — but several days did not even approach this figure. In parts of London the thermometer did not climb above freezing point for nine consecutive days.

At Clacton, the snow covered the ground on five mornings in December, 21 days in January and 20 days in February. Earls Colne had a total of 62 days with complete snow cover.

Bird life suffered considerably. Emaciated bodies of thrushes, redwings and blackbirds were found on farm tracks. Some birds abandoned their usual shyness in the quest for food and, at Burnham, a woodpecker flew into a kitchen to look for scraps. Thrushes were seen trying to crack open winkles on the foreshore.

Across London there were power cuts as a result of industrial action by Electricity Board workers, and a record demand. By 22nd January, as many as 200 London buses were put out of action when diesel froze in the engines. Next day, ice floes were seen at Tower Bridge. At Stanstead Abbots the temperature fell to a numbing -5F (-20C), while at Earls Colne it was 3F (-16C) and at Writtle, near Chelmsford, 0F (-18C).

Some people were curious to know why the Thames did not freeze as it had done so often in the past when frost fairs were held on the ice. The reason was that, in 1831, the old London Bridge was taken down and replaced, in 1835, by a new bridge with much wider arches. This enabled the water to flow through much faster than before and gave it less chance to freeze. Also, power stations were emitting warm water into the river and dredging operations were in progress — contributing to an increased flow. In parts of London, the temperature of the Thames water was 50F (10C) during the sub-zero period.

At Southend, however, seven miles of foreshore was frozen. The ice stretched 650 feet out to sea at Shoeburyness where, to add to the chill, the wind gusted at 75 mph on 19th January. By 6th February, it was feared that seven weeks of frost had killed between 60 and 70 per cent of the local oysters in their beds. It was so cold near Burnham that eggs were freezing in indoor larders.

Despite the hibernal conditions, January was the driest since 1881 in parts of England and sunshine was abundant. January was also the fourth coldest month since 1700 and February the fifth coldest. Together, the two months provided the second coldest period, for this time of the year, since records began. Only 1684 had a more severe spell of frost — and, in that year, pack ice from the Arctic blocked the English Channel!

Fishing skipper, Stan Osborne walked home from work on 22nd January, 1963 — across the sea. It was perhaps the most amazing picture of all the pictures of this extraordinary winter. The ice extended half a mile out from the shore at Leigh-on-Sea causing boats to freeze solid and launches to hold fast. Fisherman Stan did the best he could under the circumstances but the cockle industry suffered greatly.

"The drowned and desolate world lies dumb and white in a trance of snow." This quotation from Elizabeth Chase (1886) perfectly sums up this scene of a street in Clacton early in 1963. A motor car is abandoned, telegraph wires droop under the weight of their icy mantle, packed, crusty, well-trodden snow covers the highway and, in the distance, huddled figures hurry to the warmth of their home. This was the coldest winter since 1740 and Clacton, together with most of Essex, has come to a standstill.

The sea was frozen at Southend — and it was frozen at Harwich where this picture was taken on 27th January. The two vessels near the Trinity House Pier are 'Patricia' and 'Ready'.

The River Colne at Wivenhoe in January 1963, when it was possible to walk across the ice.

The Mi Amigo, converted into a radio station and silenced twice by the sea, now lies in the Long Sand.

Pirate is silenced by the sea

12th January 1966 and 20th March 1980

ATTEMPTS by both the British and Dutch governments to silence the pirate radio ship Radio Caroline, which broadcast off the North Essex coast, repeatedly failed in the 1960s and, it seemed the only threat to its existence was the weather.

On 19th January 1966, a vicious snow-laden wind hit the radio ship— *Mi Amigo*, an old Dutch coaster — so hard that it broke from its moorings and blew ashore on the beach near Chevaux de Frise Point at Great Holland. The conditions on this January day were so appalling that the Walton lifeboatmen had enormous difficulty in launching a rescue attempt and the inspector's report concluded: "The coxswain and his crew showed courage, determination and skill in boarding the lifeboat in conditions of wind and bitter cold which were the worst known for many years at this exposed station".

Despite their valiant efforts the lifeboat could not make the rescue but had to stand by while the *Mi Amigo's* men were brought ashore by the line rigged by the team operating the Life Saving Apparatus, better known as the breeches buoy.

At last, the pirate had been silenced, but not for long. The *Mi Amigo* was repaired, its lofty mast replaced and Radio Caroline was in place again, 13 miles off the Essex coast at Southend - just outside the territorial waters of the United Kingdom. By the end of the 70s a crew of four men were running the station and broadcasting on a powerful transmitter.

On Thursday 20th March 1980 Radio Caroline went aground again — this time in a storm that blew the ship, anchor, cable and all, off its mooring and onto the notorious Long Sand, graveyard of so many ships. Here the anchor caught with the disc-jockey crew unaware of the danger they were in.

The Sheerness lifeboat station was alerted and the *Helen Turnbull* was sent out at full speed into the teeth of a force nine gale. The sea was so rough that mountainous waves had to be climbed and speed reduced because the boat was shipping so much water. The lifeboat eventually reached *Mi Amigo*. It was lying on the Long Sand and being pitched and tossed by heavy rollers. The tide was rising rapidly.

Because of the dreadful seas, the rescue attempt was fraught with immense danger. Time after time the lifeboatmen attempted to get close to the stricken ship, now being overwhelmed by the sea, but great waves kept lifting up the *Helen Turnbull* and slamming it against the ship's side. Eventually all four men were pulled to safety — the last one from a stanchion to which he had been clinging for dear life. One more wave was enough to lift the *Mi Amigo* high and then down into the sand where she sank.

The coxswain said afterwards: "The operation to get the crew off took 12 hours. It was the hairiest rescue I've ever done". The disc jockeys were then taken to the police station and warned that they faced prosecution under the Marine Broadcasting (Offences) Act. The pirate radio ship, was now in the national waters of the United Kingdom!

Worst floods since 1953

14th - 15th September, 1968

THE weekend had started quietly enough with cloudy skies and just a moderate breeze. In the early hours of Sunday morning, however, rain began to fall, gently at first but building up into a storm of tropical intensity that continued almost unabated for most of the day. By Monday, valleys, towns, villages, hamlets and farms were under water — fast-flowing water that seemed to embrace everything within its reach. Huge lakes spread out over hundreds of acres of low lying land from Essex to the Hampshire-Sussex border. The Grays-Thurrock area alone received a colossal seven inches (175mm) of rain, or a third of their annual total.

The culprit had been a rapidly deepening area of low pressure to the south west of Britain which produced a pronounced 'trough' across to the south east, along which there were large-scale vertical motions of the atmosphere. Worse still it remained stationary all day on 15th September — and that meant prolonged, heavy rain.

The arrival of this weather system was heralded by a spectacular thunderstorm during Saturday afternoon. Rain cascaded onto already saturated ground. Southend, for instance, had received only 75 per cent of average sunshine during the summer, yet rainfall had been 30 per cent above average. The torrential rain fell with such force that, at Purleigh, south of Maldon 2.23 inches (57mm) was recorded in just 42 minutes. This intensity was estimated to be expected on one day in about 200 years. More than 200 chickens were drowned as rising waters inundated the broiler sheds at Lower Barn Farm, Purleigh.

The storm died down but a renewed burst of thunderstorms swept in from the Thames Estuary before midnight and continued for most of Sunday. The result was the worst flooding in the county since the disaster of 1953.

Police patrolled the flooded streets of Southend in motor boats, protecting evacuated houses from looters. Earlier, children had been handed out of first-floor windows to waiting firemen. At. Rayleigh, what looked like a raft on the river was, in fact, the roof of a pumping station located on the intersection of the A130 (Chelmsford to Southend) and the main Southend arterial. Here the water was 14 feet deep.

One bus driver defied all the odds and brought his passengers through swirling waters to their destination. Due to lightning damage on the railway between Wickford and Rayleigh, an Eastern National bus was hired to take passengers to Southminster. Driver David Dockerill did not know the roads but realised it was probably going to be a hazardous journey. He passed many abandoned vehicles and the climax came when he reached the bottom of the hill on the Fambridge side of Woodham. Driver Dockerill moved all passengers to the top deck assuming that the lower saloon would be flooded. He was right. Water surged in but he chugged bravely through the torrent.

Another obstacle was at a spot called The Whalebone. Here, the bus ploughed through the inky, black waters and the headlights of the vehicle almost disappeared. The whole bottom deck was awash but driver Dockerill constantly revved the engine to prevent the ingress of water into the exhaust pipe. Having made it across another 'lake' he opened the emergency exit to drain the water from the inside of the bus and was nearly swept off his feet by the gush.ing water.

Elsewhere, communications were completely severed. A railway bridge collapsed at Rochford and Canvey Island was isolated for some hours when the main road was under four feet of water. The Southend to Chelmsford road at Battlesbridge was impassable to all but amphibious vehicles and a queue of traffic built up to six miles long. More than 100 vehicles were abandoned in Southend and Hullbridge and members of a sailing club in Southend used their dinghies to rescue 19 people in Thornford Gardens.

During Sunday the almost Stygian gloom was punctuated at intervals by vivid flashes of lightning and reverberating thunder. All the time there was unremitting rain. The WVS in Benfleet went to work and opened a hall to provide refreshments and bedding to those who had escaped from flooded homes. At Tilbury, there were 200 emergency calls and the army helped the hard-pressed emergency services. Between 6 pm on Saturday and 6 pm on Sunday, Southend received 3.74 inches (96mm) of rain — the heaviest daily total since records were first kept in 1907.

Mayflower Hospital, Billericay, suffered loss of heating when six feet of floodwater swamped the building's heater ducts. Emergency heating was provided and it was certainly needed for the temperature did not rise above 55F (13C) all day.

The weather continued to be unsettled for the rest of the month and on 23rd September, lightning hit a transformer at Writtle County Primary School. A

Mr C.J.Smith, his wife and daughter in the lounge of their flooded home at Tilbury. The family were one of many to suffer from the deluge of 15th September, 1968.

30-foot long shed was propelled over a 15-foot hedge, over some telephone wires and across the Margaretting Road into the garden of a house. By the end of the month Southend had recorded four times its average rainfall.

The total damage of the September floods in the south east was estimated to be £6 million. Unusually large amounts of sea-ice in the Iceland - Greenland area could have been responsible for inducing a larger than average thermal or temperature gradient around Britain. This could have triggered the infamous rainstorms. Whatever the cause, it was a year that many people will never forget.

Right: A flooded bungalow in the village of Hullbridge, near Rayleigh.

CHAPTER TEN 1970 - 1979

Window on the seventies

1970: Thick snowstorms on the 12th February and 4th March caused power lines to collapse and left Chelmsford without electricity for some time. Up to nine inches of snow fell. This year also had a classic white Christmas with heavy snow falling on 25th and 26th December.

1971: A cold north-easterly airstream early in March led to a maximum temperature of only 30F (-1C) at Romford on the 6th. August was a dull month and parts of Essex experienced some heavy downpours. At Walthamstow, early on the 5th, 2.29 inches (58mm) fell — equivalent to a month's rainfall.

1972: A brief taste of sharp winter cold affected Essex on the last few days of January plunging the temperature down to below 10F (-12C) in the Ilford and Romford district. It was accompanied by several inches of snow which quickly thawed. By 5th February, the temperature had risen to 50F (10C). Violent storms with tornados affected East Anglia including Essex on the 1st August. At Chingford, there were several fatalities caused by lightning.

1973: After one of the driest winter and spring periods on record, parts of the county experienced a remarkable rainfall on 21st May. An observing station at Harold Hill measured 1.6 inches (41mm) in just 30 minutes. Brentwood railway station was inundated and trains were halted by floodwater at Gidea Park.

1974: December was the mildest since 1934 in many parts and, at Witham, it was warmer than October. There were no frosts in autumn or the first part of winter at Southend, the first time since at least 1922. Dahlias were in bloom and snowdrops out. However, the Queen Mother received a wet reception on 21st November in Chelmsford as torrential rain lashed the town. Nearly two inches of rain fell and her umbrella had a hole in it !

1975: After a mild winter, spring brought some harsh conditions with six inches of snow at Dunmow on 9th April while, on 2nd June, play was halted by snow in a county cricket match between Essex and Kent at Castle Park, Colchester. By 12th June, Colchester recorded nearly 80F (26C) and a sunny, warm summer followed.

1976: The year, best known for its great summer heatwave and drought, started with a severe gale. During the evening of 3rd January it blew a Piper Cherokee aircraft, parked on a runway at Southend Airport, over the boundary fence on to the railway line where it hit electricity cables and burst into flames. Fortunately no-one was injured.

1977: Violent thunderstorms on the night of 14th June led Essex Fire Brigade to receive 400 calls for assistance due to flooding and fires. One particularly unpleasant flash of lightning struck the fire brigade headquarters in Brentwood. Altogether more than 100 transformers were damaged and the village of Cock Clarks was without electricity for 20 hours. Chelmsford recorded 2.27 inches (58mm) of rain. At Writtle, 1.5 inches fell in under an hour.

1978: In what was a particularly varied weather year, October was outstanding. It is normally one of the wettest months but only 0.06 inches (1.7mm) fell all month at Colchester — the driest October for more than 100 years.

1979: A year full of variety. It began with 10 'ice days' at Leigh-on-Sea, a rare event at this coastal location, and continued with five days of snow in May. During the last weekend of that month, winds gusted to more than 55 knots and played havoc with the Marconi Sailing Club race meeting, capsizing many dinghies. Two men managed to swim ashore in separate incidents after being thrown overboard. Bradwell coastguard's inflatable rescue boat took a pounding and crew members were badly bruised. It was quieter in November when dense fog caused Essex police to open a special operations room in Chelmsford as visibility was reduced to just five yards in places. Earlier in August, a tornado funnel cloud moved north-east across Stanford-le-Hope and Vange.

> One sign of a change in the Essex climate concerns the lack of snow in October, compared to the nineteenth century. On 7th October, 1974, after a cold night, sleet was reported at Harlow between 9 and 9.30 am. Snow also fell on this day at Romford, Stansted and Brentwood. It was the earliest snow of the century but, unlike October falls of the last century, it didn't settle.

Dreaming of a white Christmas

GLEEFUL children looked out of their windows on Christmas morning 1970 to find several inches of snow creating a white winter wonderland outside.

At last, the festive season looked like the pictures on the Christmas cards and families quickly dragged out their toboggans, looking for the better slopes, some wishing they lived in a more undulating county than Essex. However, those in Leigh enjoyed the cliffs and youngsters revelled in the snow at Chalkwell Park and Billericay's Lake Meadows.

For drivers it was not so much fun. The Southend Arterial Road was blocked for a time at East Horndon and for the AA in Essex it was the busiest Christmas period they had known. About 160 drivers broke down on Christmas Eve and Christmas Day and the figure rose to 126 on Boxing Day alone.

An RAF helicopter rescued two Essex anglers when their motorboat was grounded in the River Blackwater during a snow squall. The men from Goldhanger and Latchingdon went out on Christmas night for a 10-hour fishing trip and failed to return home. The coastguard rescue HQ at Walton-on-the-Naze became concerned and a helicopter was sent out with the Clacton lifeboat The men were winched to safety but were found to be suffering from exposure.

Like the ones I used to know?

So 1970 was a white Christmas. "Just like the ones I used to know", goes the most favourite festive song of all, "where treetops glisten and children listen, to hear the sleigh bells in the snow."

A lovely nostalgic melody but climatically inaccurate as far as Essex and England is concerned, for only three "classic" white Christmases have occurred since 1900, despite the recollections of older people who have frequently declared they were the rule, rather than the exception "when I was a child."

The possibility of a white Christmas was greatest at the end of the eighteenth century and during the first decade of the nineteenth when there was a one in four chance of snow lying on at least two of the three Christmas days. Charles Dickens (born 1812) was probably influenced by some very real memories in his late teens.

The most likely white Christmases were those prior to the reform of the calendar in 1752 and that is where the legend really comes from. Christmas then fell on what is now 6th January — and, of course, there has always been much more snow around in the first two weeks of January than the last two in December.

The criteria for a white Christmas is that snow must fall and settle on Christmas Day. Seldom are they local affairs, for snow at this time of the year invariably involves much of the country and is usually part of a broad pattern extending over most of Scandinavia and the Continent.

The table on the right shows the three proper white Christmases in Essex and some of the "near misses" of the twentieth century.

A cyclist in Friday Wood, Colchester on Boxing Day, 1981 during the annual race against the joggers. This was the last occasion that snow was seen in Essex over the Christmas period.

WHITE CHRISTMASES IN ESSEX

1906: Several inches

1927: Typical snowstorm

1938: Snow fell every day from 15th December

1970: Between four to eight inches. A typical white Christmas

Some slight falls occurred in 1917, 1923 and 1956. In 1981, snow lay several inches deep but it had fallen before Christmas Day which was sunny with blue skies.

What was described by the newspapers as a "freak storm" occurred in Essex on 3rd May, 1973. The headlines were wrong, for this particular "freak" was due to nothing more than a storm of normal intensity moving more slowly than usual. However, it was violent enough to flood rooms in the House of Commons and give drivers a nightmarish time on flooded roads. At Southend, 1.2 inches (30mm) fell..

During the weekend of 5th-6th May, 1973, storms, squalls and high water caused 20 yachts to capsize in Thorpe Bay and, later in the month, stormy weather returned to inland areas. On 21st May, 20 people were trapped in their Chelmsford homes after flash flooding. Pupils at a Billericay school escaped unhurt when lightning hit the playground only three feet from where one boy was standing.

FROM THE EVENING GAZETTE: 22ND NOVEMBER, 1974

Homes flooded, roads closed as rains hit Essex

by GAZETTE REPORTERS

WITH flood levels rising by the hour, waterlogged Essex is facing another bout of the relentless rain that has brought chaos to the county.

About one and a half inches of rain saturated the county and most of the South-East in a day-long torrential downpour.

An RAC spokesman today described the Home Counties as the "Lake District of the south".

Roads were closed, homes flooded and farmers' fields turned into lakes.

Many towns and villages — including Chelmsford, the county town — were sealed off. Traffic on many roads is still paralysed.

And the grim forecast from the London Weather Centre today was: "More heavy rain for some time to come."

At Coggeshall, houses in Colne Road and Tey Road were flooded. Families had to move upstairs.

Salcott was under two feet of water and completely cut off last night. A boat was used in the streets to distribute sandbags and pick up stranded people.

Furious families at Latchingdon hit out at Maldon District Council and the Anglian Water Authority as their homes lay beneath a foot of floodwater and sewage.

May 1975 and more floods in Essex after 36 hours of heavy rain, commencing on 16th May. Picture shows an Eastern National bus negotiating the water which collected under the railway bridge in Rectory Road, Ashingdon. It was one of many incidents — the Spur Road, Rayleigh underpass was under seven feet of water, the Horse and Groom public house at Rochford was inundated and Rayleigh firemen responded to 50 calls to pump out flooded gardens.

The average rainfall for May is about 1.6 inches (40 mm.) Stanford-le-Hope equalled this in just one day, while Writtle 1.4 inches (35 mm), Southend 1.3 inches (32 mm) and Shoeburyness 1.2 inches (31 mm) had enought to wonder why Essex has a reputation for being one of the driest counties in England.

Cricket match suspended—snow in June!

A county cricket match at Castle Park, Colchester between Kent and Essex on 2nd June, 1975 was halted due to snow. The umpires who adjudicated on this bizarre, and most unusual spectacle, consulted Law 3, sub-section 14D of cricket's book of rules: "The umpires should suspend play only when they consider conditions are so bad that it is unreasonable or dangerous to continue." This was unreasonable. It was snowing in Colchester in June.

It was not the only occasion that Essex county cricketers have been taken off the field during a first class match for circumstances other than rain. On 24th April, 1981, which was one of the coldest and snowiest of the twentieth century over much of the British Isles, the weather was so cold that the match at Fenners against Cambridge University was suspended. While play was possible, the players wore two sweaters and woolly caps. But the wind, which was between north and east was so bitter that bowlers were unable to grasp the ball and fielders were immobilised by frozen fingers. The umpires conferred again. This was unreasonable.

The June snow of 1975 prompted an AA spokesman in Essex to warn motorists to make sure they had anti-freeze in their radiators. Anglia TV weatherman, Michael Hunt said: "On a superficial examination, I have no record of snow in June south of the Wash this century." He blamed the persistent high pressure to the north

of the British Isles for causing the icy winds.

Ironically, 1975, when the first World Cup was played in England and Australia were the tourists, was a long hot vintage summer for cricket enthusiasts. The snow in Colchester did not last long. By 12th June, people in Castle Park were basking in temperatures of 80F (26C).

Between the summer heatwaves of 1975 and 1976, there was a brief cold spell in December as high pressure led to frosty nights with some freezing fog. At Little Parndon, the mercury dropped to just 18F (-8C) and there was a spate of traffic accidents between Chelmsford and Rivenhall due to fog and ice on the A12. The police closed a 10-mile stretch of the road. At sea, the conditions were diabolical and several vessels took refuge by Southend pier. The photograph was taken at Burnt Mills Lane, Basildon.

January gale destroys homes

2nd January, 1976

WINDS of near hurricane force tore through Essex on the night of 2nd January, 1976. Across Britain, 24 people died in this historic storm.

The weather had been rough for several days. Christmas tinsel, draped in front rooms, often quivered as draughts screamed through rattling windows. The gale on the evening of the 2nd etched itself on people's minds for many years. It was even compared to the great 1703 hurricane, considered to be the most damaging storm ever recorded.

A deep area of low pressure moved across Scotland into the North Sea causing terrific winds — up to 134 mph in Strathclyde. Although the gusts were not as powerful in Essex, they were strong enough to reach 82 mph at Stansted, damage buildings and leave the countryside strewn with wreckage.

In the Colchester area, four houses were partially demolished and a house was blown down in Wivenhoe High Street. Homes in Morton Road, Colchester and Albany Road, West Bergholt lost their gable ends. A chimney crashed through the roof of another dwelling in Wilson Marriage Road. In one bizarre incident, a woman was blown over in Wivenhoe — and watched £130 in notes blow from her purse and disappear.

At Brightlingsea, racing catamarans, belonging to the British Olympic sailing squad were wrecked. Within half an hour of the switchboard opening on Monday morning, 5th January, Colchester Council had handled 200 distress calls from council tenants. Tendring Council reported that up to 200 council house roofs were damaged and five chimney stacks destroyed.

At Great Bromley, a car was crushed by a falling tree — one of many which suffered the same fate across the county. At Black Notley, a Morris Traveller parked in a lay-by was written off when a heavy tree fell through the middle of the vehicle.

As with the storms of January, 1953 and 1962, this depression produced a storm surge in the North Sea but, fortunately, it did not coincide with a high tide, so damage was limited.

The market stalls at Pitsea were torn to shreds by the gale of 2nd January, 1976

Take a bath with a friend!

Blazing summer of 1976

THE summer of 1976 has a place in the record books for its great heat, abundance of sunshine and drought.

It was the time when, owing to a serious water shortage caused by the hot weather, people were advised to share a bath with a friend and put a brick in the cistern. And it was the time when a drought minister was appointed by the Government and — as he took office — it rained cats and dogs!

A foretaste of that magnificent summer came early in May when the temperature soared into the 80's F. But the overwhelming heat did not come until June. By the end of that month the temperatures were in the nineties.

It was so hot on 23rd June that pupils marched out of Nicholas School, Laindon complaining of the suffocating conditions. The sun was so strong at Southend that roads melted and had to be gritted by the local council. At Maldon, 90 F (32C) was recorded. Dozens of people across the county collapsed in the heat and ambulancemen advised elderly people to wear wide-brimmed Mexican hats to ward off the harmful rays of the sun. That night at Shoebury, the temperature fell to no lower than 64 F (18C), making it the warmest June night there for 19 years.

Some folk who tried to cool off by wading over the mudflats of the Thames Estuary to reach deep water found themselves in the middle of a busy shipping route and had to be rescued.

On 24th June, the temperature at Basildon reached 92F (33C), sparking an enormous demand for beer and soft drinks at the town's Bass Charrington depot. Next morning, the temperature at Pitsea had reached 85F (30C) by 10.30 am, but this was put in the shade by later events. It was so hot that morning in London that passengers at Baker Street panicked, fainted and smashed windows to breathe when some 400 of them were trapped for nearly two hours in a packed underground train.

The capital sweltered that day and by 3 pm the mercury had climbed to 93F (34C), but the following day was hotter still. On 26th June, it rocketed to 95F (35C) in Holborn. By 10 am, it had already surged to a blistering 84F (29C) after Londoners had experienced their hottest June night for 29 years with the coolest part of the night an uncomfortable 70F (21C).

Clacton bathed in more than 14 hours of sunshine a day and enjoyed a top temperature of 80F. Even the sea breeze was unable to lower the temperature because the persistent European anticyclone was directing hot air up across France and feeding it to the east coast. Many holidaymakers at Clacton, Walton and Frinton suffered from sunstroke and a few from heatstroke, which was more serious. This occurred when the local air temperature rose above body temperature.

In Colchester, policemen were allowed on the beat without their ties but firemen, wearing helmets and heavy tunics, sweltered throughout as more and more calls came in from town and countryside. Southend firemen were also busy. On 29th July, Southend Pier was alight and 500 people had to be rescued in boats and trains while, from the air, water was directed onto the flames from an aircraft. Southend was also pestered by a plague of black flies, attracted to the many hundreds of rose bushes in the town centre.

There was some relief from the oppressive conditions when fierce thunderstorms broke out over Essex on Thursday night, 15th July. But despite the St Swithin's legend, it did not rain for a further 40 days thereafter.

The storms brought nearly an inch of rain in two hours — a third of the year's total so far that year. Emergency services answered hundreds of calls to flooded homes and roads. Power cuts hit Southend, Canewdon, Billericay and Wickford, affecting 4,800 homes.

Lightning hit the home of Mr Malcolm Warrington in Perry Street, Billericay, and the family had to flee the house as flames took hold. In Wickford, the water lay four feet deep in the Southend Road. Police had to rescue drivers marooned under the railway arches in Hockley and Battlesbridge. The Crest Avenue council estate in Pitsea was evacuated as floodwater poured into homes.

Another storm struck parts of Essex on 20th July but, by midnight on 23rd July, the use of hosepipes was banned and once again the countryside became tinder dry.

A tidal wave of flames spread across a field at Chatham Green and destroyed three homes and badly damaged two others. The months of June, July and August were considered to be the best for warmth and sunshine since at least 1868 in many parts of Britain. Soon after the appointment of Dennis Howe as Minister for Drought, the weather broke and September provided welcome heavy rain which helped to replenish reservoirs which had completely emptied during the summer.

Most ponds, lakes and reservoirs had dried up in the heat but, on 20th August 1976, firemen found a pond with enough muddy water to help put out this barn blaze near Chelmsford. It was one of many fires in what was to be a record year for the Essex fire brigade The great heat also led to many homes cracking up. At one stage, in early July, 400 Essex firemen were engaged at the same time in their busiest week for 30 years.

The Essex Weather Forecast

When the BBC television programme *Weekend* promoted a contest for new East Anglian songs, a selection of entries was later published by Yoxford Publications. Entitled *New Songs for East Anglia*, it included this ditty of Henry Hinds, set to the tune of *Bunessan* (Morning Has Broken). It is entitled The Essex Weather Forecast.

Morning has broken in Thorpe-le-Soken
But there's a haze at Walton-on-Naze
Snow is descending at Weeley and Tendring
With frostbitten toes at Beaumont-cum-Noze

Pressure is falling, the weather's appalling
By about six, you'll get it at Wix
Drive very gently round Frating and Bentley
The weather looks bleak till the end of the week

Tomorrow morning, just about dawning
Clouds will be forming o'er Clacton-on-Sea
Here's something funny, it's suddenly sunny
Over Harwich and old Parkeston Quay

As the Mediterranean climate persisted throughout the summer of 1976, people tried to cool off by wading into rivers, lakes ponds and even the mudflats of the Thames Estuary. No-one bothered about Bulphan Pond, near Basildon and, little wonder — it was bone dry. The residents (pictured above) look very confused. The world, they thought, has gone quite quackers!

Sliding to a standstill with a metallic thud!

12th-13th January, 1977

IT was only a two-hour blizzard but it was so fierce, so unrelenting and so unfair in its timing that it brought to North Essex, in particular, a day of total chaos. The first flakes fell at breakfast time and slowly life slithered to a standstill, on occasions with a metallic thud. There were accidents galore, traffic jams in excess of eight miles built up on all roads leading into Colchester. Workers attempting to walk to factory or office gave up and, in Brightlingsea, almost 1,000 children were given the day off.

As temperatures plunged, large powdery flakes settled and weathermen warned of hazardous days to follow, Essex prepared for a repeat performance of 1963. Everything closed down including Colchester Crown Court where a murder trial was taking place. A detective due to give evidence was involved in an accident on the way to court. He was taken to Harwich Hospital.

Suddenly it stopped snowing. Essex picked itself up, albeit slowly, and within a few days disappointed children realised that it was not going to be such a memorable winter after all.

This extraordinary photograph of a powerful whirlwind between the villages of Arkesden and Cleaver End, near Saffron Walden was taken on 10th August, 1977 by weatherman, John Banks who says that the vortex was at least 50 yards in diameter, moving northwards and curving to the left towards the village of Elmdon. It was travelling about 30 mph. At the time the sky was dark but no rain fell and the wind changed from light south-east to moderate north-west. The whirlwind was Torro Force 2, or 3. No real damage was done except for a battery casing being torn from an electric fence and immature apples being stripped from trees at Palmer's Fruit Farm.

Snow may have brought road and rail traffic to a halt but it did not deter horse riders in the more sheltered areas of Epping Forest.

Piers battered in violent gale

10th January, 1978

THERE was nothing unusual in the early January weather of 1978. Some rain, sunshine and slight frosts were about par for the course, but things took a decided turn for the worse on 10th January. What meteorologists call a "wave" on a weather front rapidly deepened and formed into an intense depression which crossed the Midlands and East Anglia on Wednesday 11th. In its wake a severe northerly gale produced a sea surge ominously like that of 1953 but, in most cases, the improved defences held firm. Nonetheless, it was a night of terror for some and the morning after saw a battered and bruised Essex coastline. Inland, a number of trees, power lines and buildings also came to grief.

The wind reached its peak during Wednesday evening. Rapidly rising pressure as the depression passed brought near hurricane-force gusts whipping up the sea into a frenzy and daylight at Walton-on-the-Naze revealed a beach littered with planks and door frames, roofing and assorted debris as 500 huts were smashed; many beyond repair. The pier was so devastated that lifeboatmen could not reach their vessel.

Another pier to suffer was that of Clacton where 100 feet of reinforced concrete flooring was washed away. The repair bill was estimated at £100,000. The Lifeboat Station took a pounding and lifeboat gear was badly damaged, forcing the boat to be removed to Brightlingsea. Overall damage to the Clacton and Walton areas was put at half a million pounds. Further afield, in Kent, the storm led to the demise of Margate and Herne Bay piers — the first light of dawn revealing a mass of crumpled girders where once-proud structures had been.

The violent winds led to very high tides. At Southend, the sea reached a level of 23 feet 2 inches, more than four feet higher than expected. At old Leigh, boats were seen plying along the High Street as water overtopped defences. The sea gushed in through gaping holes cut into Foulness's sea wall, there being as many as 20 breaches. Heavy earth moving equipment brought in by the Army's Engineer Regiment based at Colchester, managed to plug the gaps but long-term repairs were estimated to cost £250,000.

A Hullbridge family was abruptly woken by loud cries from its youngest member, six-year-old Susan, after she had paddled downstairs into icy water. The family spent the rest of the night upstairs, their telephone out of action and unable to summon help.

Meanwhile a 24-foot sailing cruiser, The Skensen, broke her moorings at Southend and ended up across the other side of the Thames Estuary at All Hallows in Kent. Inland, at Colchester, the front gable and part of the side wall of an end-of-terrace house in Papillon Road was blown out showering bricks in to the street. Up to 30,000 households lost power particularly at Little Clacton, Birch and Weeley. Several flights from Southend were cancelled due to the ferocious winds.

The alarm bells for London sounded as the capital's flood control centre became operative. The water came to within 19 inches of the top of the retaining walls bordering the Thames. Conditions would have been considerably more grave had the upper part of the river been in flood. The lesson learned from this storm was the urgent need of a flood barrier across the river. Work was already underway on the project but it was to be six more years before it was completed.

Beach huts at Frinton-on-Sea were completely wrecked.

As operation mop-up continued along the north-east Essex coast after the onslaught of the two vicious tides, a sigh of relief went round when the afternoon high tide failed to muster the strength of the night before. At Harwich, residents waited anxiously behind sandbagged doors for the high water level of 15 feet to subside. At Maldon it was even higher — a staggering 26 feet was measured by the harbourmaster, two feet higher than predicted. A Dutch coaster ran aground at Rowhedge, nine boats were washed ashore at Bradwell. including a £100,000 luxury yacht and, all along the coast, sea walls were breached. At Foulness, the enormous power of the waves punctured the wall in at least 20 places.
The Royal Engineers, based in Colchester, supplied the machinery to effect temporary repairs.
Photograph shows a victim of the flooding in Distillery Lane, Colchester receiving a fireman's lift.

A depression, which crossed the North Sea in early August 1978, brought thunderstorms and localised downpours to many areas, including Clacton where half an inch (13mm) fell on the 3rd. Here, Mr and Mrs Moody and family of Park Avenue, Eastwood mop up after a particularly vicious cloudburst.

So Essex is the driest county in Britain. Say that to the fishermen who live and work in Old Leigh, and they may tell you politely to "go away". Here is another occasion when they suffered from the vagaries of the weather — flooding at Old Leigh Victoria Wharf on 22nd March, 1979.

On this bleak day, in early January 1979, even the police were stuck at Bourne's Green Chase, Southend. The level of snow at Langham was 11 inches.

Four Benfleet fishermen lost at sea

The winter of 1978-9

THE winter of 1978-9 was to become famous not only as a winter of industrial unrest and strikes but for — vicious gales, blinding snow, traffic chaos and all the turmoil associated with a really fierce season.

It actually started late in 1978. Mild weather was blasted out of the way by piercing easterly winds and driving snow on the evening of 30th December. High tides added to the perils of snowdrifts and, at Southend alone, £200,000 of damage occurred when beach huts were washed out to sea. Old Leigh suffered, as it always does. Even the pubs were under water in this winter of discontent.

Four fishermen were lost at sea after being caught in the teeth of the gale. The men from Benfleet set off from Benfleet Creek when the weather was benign, just hours before the arrival of the storm. One body was washed up on the Kent coast.

Summer chalets were smashed to pieces at Westcliff and the Thames Estuary Yacht Club was seriously damaged. The A13 and A127 were blocked by snowdrifts and, for a time, Southend was completely cut off. The pier at Walton on the Naze was cut in two by high winds, isolating the lifeboat station at the end of the jetty. Great Wakering was marooned for

almost two days and snowploughs had to force a passage through the drifts at Battlesbridge and Rayleigh. Train services on the Fenchurch Street and Liverpool Street lines were blocked until snowploughs cleared the tracks.

In Maldon, families were without power for up to eight hours as blizzards brought down power lines. Canvey Island, not to be outdone by the mainland, was isolated by seven foot drifts.

New Year's Day, 1979 was brilliantly sunny but bitterly cold. The temperature struggled to reach 25F (-4C) in places. The month continued cold with some more snow but there was worse to come in February. The headlines in the East Essex Gazette on February 23rd declared: "Worst snowstorms for 21 years" — and then went on to describe the amazing height of drifts on the Colchester, Clacton, Frinton and Walton branch lines.

Volunteers trudged through three feet of snow to deliver meals on wheels around Holland-on-Sea and Jaywick after abandoning their cars. At Tendring, letters to Pilcox Lane were delivered by tractor when the postman failed to get through and, at Beaumont, three lorries and six cars were trapped — the drivers spending the night with local residents.

In parts of the Midlands, the 1978-9 winter had more snow than any year between 1939 and 1992.

Tornado at Basildon, 1979

THUNDERSTORMS, floods, blizzards — what else could be in store for Essex in this turbulent year? The answer came on August 3rd with more severe storms along the Thames Estuary which brought deluges to some places, at least one of which was accompanied by the menacing vortex of a tornado.

Here the writhing funnel is captured by Evening Echo photographer Ron Case as it passed Basildon. Disruption was caused mainly by torrential rain. At Stanford le Hope just under an inch (24mm) fell and flooding affected Southend Airport for a time.

In November, fog returned to plague the county, during a rare quiet spell in a most unsettled year. Some of the fog lingered all day on 20th-21st November and visibility was reduced to just a few yards.

Photograph shows the lights of the Oxley Green bus attempting to penetrate the murk of a most unpleasant day.

CHAPTER ELEVEN 1980 — 1989

The damp and angry eighties

1980: From the 9th to 19th May a remarkable sunny interlude gave the county around 140 hours of sunshine, or 70 per cent of the monthly average. However, in June it became stormy with thunder heard on 10 days at Leigh-on-Sea and Rayleigh. A Danbury family had a lucky escape when lightning struck the house causing a roof to collapse, but nobody was in the upper rooms at the time. Lightning in Chelmsford triggered off fire alarms, forcing people to flee out into torrential rain. November was the snowiest since 1952 and snow lay for four days.

1981: Very icy conditions on the roads between 10th and 12th January. Eight juggernauts jack-knifed near Colchester blocking all approaches. Spring was wet and a record rainfall was measured at Colchester — equal to that of 1937. Overall the summer was dry but on 9th July a severe storm struck the Brentwood district and there were 246 emergency calls to fire stations in the county. December was the coldest since 1890. The temperature fell to 4F (-15C) at Loughton and snow covered the ground for 23 days at Colchester. A blizzard on the 13th led to hundreds of cars, lorries, buses and even ambulances being abandoned.

1982: Severe weather returned in January. Snow reduced the busy A12 to a single track near Chelmsford. As the temperature plummetted to 9F (-13C) at Witham, the sea froze at Maldon and boats were held fast in ice. Essex spent £1.5 million on snow clearance during the winter. On 4th June the temperature reached 85F (29C), followed by fierce thunderstorms. At Loughton, more than three inches (79mm) fell in three hours. Around 200 houses and shops were flooded and 12 buildings struck by lightning. Later in the month a 200-year-old wind vane on top of the parish church at Rayleigh was destroyed by lightning. On 21st September, an active cold front crossed Essex accompanied by tornados. At Springfield, thousands of pounds worth of damage was caused to Rush Green Hospital. Seaweed was sucked up at Point Clear Bay and draped on houses near by.

1983: Another wet spring at Colchester and a new record rainfall (since records began in 1887) with eight inches. The countryside was so wet that farmers found it impossible to take machinery onto the waterlogged fields. July was possibly the warmest of any month back to the 17th century. At Colchester, Basildon and Loughton, the average daily maximum

reached 81F (27C). At Witham it was the driest summer since 1921.

1984: Ex-hurricane Hortense brought prolonged thunderstorms to parts of Essex, striking a house in Braintree and flooding parts of Bocking. On 9th November there was another exotic visitation — this time red dust from the Moroccan Sahara where sandstorms had raged.

1985: January was a bitter month and vessels were locked fast into the frozen River Blackwater. The temperature fell to 10F (-12C) in Colchester with snow covering the ground for over half the month. A severe hailstorm on 26th May devastated Good Easter, near Chelmsford. A new Ford Fiesta was pitted by giant hailstones over 1.5 inches in diameter and some thudded inches into soft earth. A farm at Aythorpe Roding lost £50,000 worth of crops.

1986: Winds gusting to 70 mph brought down power cables and blacked out homes in Maldon on 22nd January. Another gale on 24th March tore the roofs off two tower blocks at Great Baddow and altogether there were 145 calls to the emergency services. February was cold — never reaching more than 39F (4C) in many places. Only 1947 was colder this century. Summer was poor and the August Bank Holiday was washed out by ex-hurricane Charley, giving as much as 1.5 inches (38mm) in Loughton.

1987: In a year which saw the working day brought to a halt twice — by snow in January and the great storm in October — the summer did not provide much solace. It was wet, and powerful thunderstorms gave flash floods on 29th July especially at North Weald with 2.7 inches (68mm) in just over an hour. Essex was again buffeted on 22nd August and the Chelmsford district was all but cut off by floods.

1988: It was the wettest January at Colchester since records began in 1889 with 5.8 inches (149mm) but February was very bright with 120 hours of sun.

1989: A winter devoid of snow and so mild that blackbirds nested early in February. Barometric pressure fell to 28.20 inches (955 millibars) on 25th February, the lowest value since Christmas Day 1821. May was the driest at Shoeburyness since records began in 1921 and was the sunniest of any month at Clacton since July 1911 — a prelude to a glorious summer.

Heavy rain which accompanied a storm on July 9th, 1981 left most of south east Essex awash. One inch (25mm) fell at Rayleigh and Leigh and there was severe flooding in these and other towns and villages. Chelmsford rarely escapes on these occasions — and this was no exception. Westway was particularly hard hit and only the adventurous and foolhardy attempted to find a way through the swirling waters. London also suffered and at High Holborn, the London Weather Centre recorded an incredible 2.25 inches (58mm) of rain in 50 minutes. Pictures shows the damp situation in West Horndon, near Brentwood.

There was nothing exceptional about the summer of 1981, except that it was fairly dry. The sun shone brightly in the first week of August when Wivenhoe enjoyed its annual regatta and these little visitors found the best way to keep cool was to go topless — and bottomless! On 6th August it was pitch black in London at mid-day before a bad storm broke. The storm was followed in West Essex by three sunless days, an unusual occurrence in a summer month.

Water dripping off branches in the sunshine, froze into dazzling, clinking icicles at Seabrooks Fruit Farm, Little Leighs in mid-December, 1981. The month was noted for its low temperatures and snowfalls. Britain's lowest recorded temperature of all time was equalled when Braemar in Grampian recorded -17F (-27C) just a few weeks later on 10th January, 1982.

Going nowhere! Boats were welded by ice into their moorings at Maldon during the intense cold of January 1982. England's lowest-ever temperature occurred this month. On 10th January -15F (-26C) was measured at Newport, Shropshire.

The people of Essex, having the cold of January 1982 fresh in their minds, were delighted when 1983 began with remarkably mild weather — but things soon cooled down. Here, Southend council workmen, Jim Morgan and Harry Boswell examine the frozen sea at Southend on 23rd February 1983. Beyond them is an expanse of "frazzle" — a type of patterned sea ice. A hot summer followed and, at Shoebury, July was the warmest since 1921.

So what's new? Well there's a fallen tree which makes a jolly good climbing frame for the children of Broomfield, Chelmsford — courtesy of the high winds of April 1983 and, below, there's a rowing boat pushed into service to rescue people from their flooded homes at Hullbridge. This was in May 1983 when there was between four and five inches of rain in parts of Essex.

Flood survivors see safety swing into action

DEFENDERS: The new flood barriers look strong and protective at Benfleet, Easthaven and Fobbing.

SURVIVORS of the 1953 floods, in which 68 South East Essex people died and 25,000 were rescued by boats, were due at the opening today of Canvey's new sea defences.

The barriers are part of a £520 million scheme to protect Thameside areas and London from floods for 1,000 years.

The opening was due to be by Treasury Minister Mr John Wakeham, Tory MP for Rochford and Maldon.

Chairman of Essex River Division of the Anglian Water Authority Mr John Norris said: "This is a

By DEL FLATLEY

tremendous landmark in the magnificent efforts to ensure the 1953 tragedy is never repeated."

The Canvey defences include barriers in Vange Creek, at Fobbing and nearby Easthaven.

Flood threats

At Fobbing the giant barrier is 120ft wide and will normally be held horizontally 30ft above spring tides to let tugs and barges reach wharves at Pitsea.

Easthaven barrier will have three openings, two for the tide and a 40ft-wide centre opening for boats using the creek.

Both barriers were built by contractors John Howard for about £6½ million.

The Benfleet barrier across the creek is about 200ft downstream of the bridge near Benfleet rail station.

Other schemes have been completed substantially raising the height of Canvey sea protection walls, which will allow the islanders to sleep peacefully at night secure from flood threats.

After the official opening at Benfleet barrier a lunch was being held at Runnymede Hall, Benfleet, with speeches by Mr Norris and Sir Bernard Braine, Tory MP for South East Essex.

People will be invited to inspect the flood defences over the weekend.

Officials will be on duty to answer questions on the protection they give.

At last — hope for Canvey Island

February 1983

This page reproduced from the *Evening Echo* of 25th February, 1983 represented a red-letter day for the people of Canvey Island and all those who were living with the threat of floods in South-East Essex. Nevertheless, John Wakeham, MP for Rochford and Maldon, who unveiled the plaque, was warned that many more thousands of pounds would be needed to repair other flood defences in the county.

Chairman of Essex Rivers Division, Mr John Norris said that Essex had 220 miles of sea walls to maintain and these were built in the 1950s to protect towns, villages and farmland. "They are now well over 30 years old and we

face a terrible problem. We have now had four highly critical and dangerous high tides in a 40-year period and we'd be failing in our duty if we did not heed this warning".

Conservative MP for South-East Essex, Sir Bernard Braine, who was chairman of the committee to draw up measures to counteract the effects of the 1953 floods, said the new defences offered top protection for the people of Canvey. "During today's ceremony, the memories of the 1953 flooding came sweeping back to me. Anybody who went through that will never forget it. And nowhere was the devastation of precious homes and the loss of life and the damage

to property greater than on Canvey."

Sir Bernard paid a special tribute to the bravery and spirit of the people of Canvey and added: "I never cease to be astonished at their capacity to make a joke during these times of abject misery".

The new flood defence scheme, funded by the Government was built at a cost of £520 million and included 75 miles of sea defences and eight major barriers. It was built by the Anglian Water Authority and the Essex River Division.

Storm that cost a million pounds

26th May, 1985

THE propensity of Essex to severe hail and thunderstorms has been vividly portrayed so far. Another classic example was on 26th May, 1985, when a warm, moist, southerly airstream fed across the county ahead of advancing cooler air.

On Sunday afternoon, towering thunder clouds built up over the village of Pleshy, north-west of Chelmsford. Giant hail crashed down damaging cars, smashing greenhouses and laying waste fields of wheat and barley. Some lumps of ice were bigger than golf balls and they embedded themselves in up to two inches of soft ground.

At nearby Good Easter, farmer Tommy Matthews said his fields looked as if they had been under artillery bombardment. He had suffered £28,000 worth of damage to his broad bean crop and 100 acres of wheat lay in ruins. One house in the village had 150 slates torn from its roof and damage was along a mile-wide swathe. Many farmers were not insured against hail, despite the fact that it has taken centre stage in more than one weather incident in recent history.

Along the coast, a sudden squall led to 34 sailing dinghies capsizing in the Crouch Estuary and several turned turtle in the Blackwater. All were rescued by the Burnham Inshore Lifeboat and Bradwell Coastguards. A burst of rain at Chelmsford gave 0.6 inches (17mm) in just 15 minutes and a huge lake appeared across the Rainsford Road.

Altogether, the storm caused £1.5 million worth of damage to crops. The Agriculture Minister Michael Jopling paid a special visit to mid-Essex in response to compensation claims. One farmer at Good Easter said that 60 acres of his winter barley were destroyed in less than 20 minutes and that "seeing is believing" to really grasp the extent of the devastation.

However, the minister gave cold comfort to them, so a "Hail Disaster Fund" was set up by the Essex branch of the National Farmers Union to help the most needy.

The summer did not provide much solace either, for it was the sixth wettest at Colchester since 1887 and, at Rayleigh, 9.2 inches (232mm) fell — the wettest summer since 1958.

Good Easter farmer, Tommy Matthews with some of the giant hailstones which fell on Sunday 26th May, 1985.

The Agriculture Minister visits a hail-hit farm at Good Easter where the wheat crop was devastated.

An uncomfortable day for sailors and their ships on March 24th, 1986. The preceding month had been the coldest February since the memorable winter of 1947.

Frozen February was replaced by Menacing March when a gale on the 24th blew so strongly that two roofs were blown off tower blocks at The Vineyards, Great Baddow and there were more than 145 calls for assistance to the emergency services.

A real taste of Siberia

January 1987

ON Saturday 10th January, 1987 snowflakes began to fall on Essex. Some 48 hours later the county was paralysed. No buses, no trains, no milk, no post, no schools and, in many places, no telephones. Major roads were closed, villages were isolated, animals lost and people who dared to venture outside, donned their moonboots and later still walked on the tops of hedges. The whole county slithered to a standstill in the most chaotic conditions since 1963.

Early in the New Year there were ominous signs that something unusual was about to happen, meteorologically. On 5th January, temperatures in Finland were around -31F (-35C) and the frigid air was heading our way. Further east, in Siberia, thermometers registered -76F. By Saturday 10th January, temperatures were falling steadily. The wind had swung round to the north-east. a huge high pressure system was established over Scandinavia and the stage was set for a real Siberian winter.

On Sunday, those heavy flakes soon built up a layer several inches deep and the BBC weather forecast for the week ahead was dire. Over the next few days the cold intensified. On Monday, Southend remained at just 14F (-10C) for much of the day and the sea froze along a 700 yard stretch of the beach at Westcliff. This Monday was the coldest, with the lowest daytime maximum, of the century so far, and for snow to fall at such low temperatures was almost unprecedented.

Myriads of fine powdery flakes whirled in from the North Sea, generated by its relative warmth. Rising columns of air, cooling and condensing, produced almost non-stop snow showers throughout Tuesday and a huge clearance operation was quickly under way. Throughout Essex, snowploughs, gritters and thousands of men swept into action. In South East Essex they drew on supplies of nearly 60,000 tons of salt — and they were needed. By 14th January, Southend had accumulated two feet of level snow with 18 inches at Thundersley and nearly as much at Leigh-on-Sea.

Worse was to follow as the wind strengthened and whipped up the loose, powdery snow so that Wednesday was a day of both magic and mayhem. The savage winds roared over fields, whipping up the snow into blinding clouds. Drifts, many feet deep, blocked roads and numerous cars were abandoned. Some were completely buried. Mersea, Tiptree, Halstead and Maldon were cut off. All villages between Clacton and Lowestoft were isolated as the drifts built up higher and higher.

There was panic buying from the shops — people squabbling over the last loaf of bread. Postal deliveries and collections came to a halt as did the buses. Four hundred out of 700 schools in the county were closed and 150,000 children had the chance to enjoy some wonderful days.

At Lawford near Manningtree, a baby was born in an ambulance which had become stuck fast in a four-foot snow drift. A police Landrover and snowplough tried in vain to reach them but the story ended well as little Rachel and her mother were rescued.

During the days that followed, dedication and duty were fully tested. At St John's Hospital, Chelmsford, staff stayed overnight to ensure full medical care was maintained. Essex Social Services operated a "snow cabinet" which co-ordinated help to the needy. Bleary-eyed broadcasters on Radio Essex and BBC Essex operated special snowlines dealing with thousands of distress calls and there were appeals for people with four-wheel vehicles to deliver emergency supplies to hospitals.

Many drivers met with difficulties and at the AA control centre at Stanmore, 4,000 emergency calls were logged. One totally buried car was bulldozed out of a drift at Southminster with the driver still inside. A patrol man saw just one traveller on the A12 with no apparent problem; he was ski-ing in the fast lane near Chelmsford! On the railways, conditions were just as testing with only a shuttle service on most lines. However, at Ingatestone there was a problem of a different kind when a train from Harwich actually caught fire and passengers had to disembark.

With so many roads impassable, a helicopter was used to ferry in electrical engineers to help restore supplies to the St Lawrence Bay area, and Essex ambulances were given an extra crew member armed with a shovel to help dig a path through the snow.

Slowly, slowly, the wind abated and by Friday there was a chance to dig away the snow without the drifts returning. It was a strange world. Icicles festooned houses leading to the demise of many gutters, but the milkmen returned and so did the postmen.

Inevitably as the thaw came there was a spate of burst pipes — and 250 calls in one day to the Essex Fire Brigade to deal with flooded property.

Ice floes bob among snowbound boats at moorings at Leigh-on-Sea on 13th January, 1987.

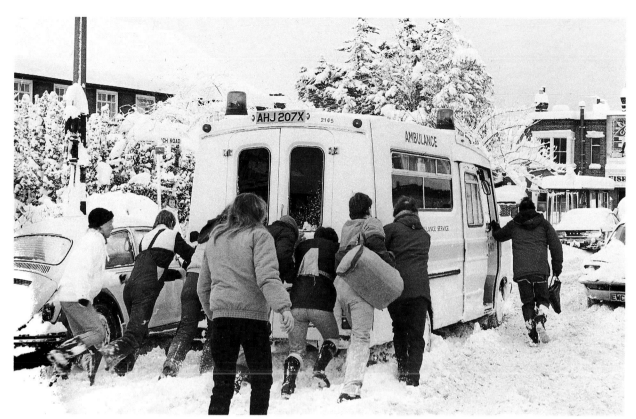

An ambulance stuck in the snow but plenty of help was on hand. This is Southchurch on 13th January, 1987

Still and white in a trance of snow. This is how Leigh-on-Sea looked from the air in mid-January, 1987, showing St Clement's Church.

The bright lights of Southend glow even brighter on a world of sharp pale shadows, perfect curves and fresh deep snow. The reflected lights are intense and multitudinous and it looks quite heavenly — unless you're outside! This was taken at Southchurch Road in January 1987 near The Deepings underpass.

Cars and vans are spreadeagled at curious angles but the bread queue is straight and determined. Great Wakering from the air in January 1987's remarkable freeze-up.

Stormy days — then Big Daddy!

July - August 1987

THE summer of 1987 was fairly typical — promising in short bursts, but cool and then unsettled. Also par for the course was the usual ration of Essex thunderstorms. Some of them, however, were rather savage and several areas were lashed by hail, struck by lightning and then flooded — in that order!

A violent storm swept the Epping district on 29th July in what had begun as a relatively showery and innocuous weather situation, with nothing to suggest the intensity of rain which was to cascade down in the early afternoon. Around two inches (50mm) fell in just 20 minutes at Thornwood Common. Water reached a depth of nine feet under the motorway bridge on the Epping to North Weald Road. A transit van had just its roof showing above the water on the A414 and a stretch of carriageway was closed on the M11.

A small stream at Cobbins Brook rose six feet in 30 minutes and became a raging torrent. Fields of rape were flattened by hail and one farmer had to rescue his wife and children from an upstairs room by ladder.

Calls to the Essex Fire and Rescue Headquarters totalled 150 in an hour and at Waltham Abbey, police patrolled the area in dinghies hired from the Thames River Police. Damage amounted to thousands of pounds.

Conditions were ripe for thunderstorms on 22nd August. The mercury had topped 84F (29C) at Southend and Colchester, it was humid and there was cool air aloft. During the afternoon, massive cumulo-nimbus clouds thrust up to 36,000 feet, nearly seven miles high. No wonder there was almost total darkness underneath them.

There had been storms the previous evening but the big one arrived during the heat of the afternoon. Keen weather observer, Malcolm May of Chelmsford described what happened: "At about 3 pm, huge towering clouds were visible to the south west and the sky became very dark with shades of olive green and purple. Lightning was violent and thunder deafening. This was the Big Daddy I had been expecting. The rain began at 3 pm with huge drops. It was like night time and all the street lights came

Chelmsford, where the town was cut off for a time on 22nd August, 1987

on. By now, torrents of water were falling as if someone had turned a giant bucket of water upside down.

"I ventured out of doors and measured a 50 mph gust of wind, but marble-sized hail was falling, and I hastily retreated. The thunder was so loud it sounded like wardrobes being thrown down the stairs. Floodwater was building up rapidly round the house and I had to start baling it away from the patio to prevent it coming inside. At 4.20 it eased off but by now fire engines were sounding in all directions. Just over two inches (52mm) of hail had fallen in 40 minutes."

No wonder Chelmsford was cut off for a time. Seven feet of water covered the Army and Navy roundabout as the Rivers Chelmer and Can burst their banks.

Further afield, at Tiptree, floods inundated 15 homes and forced manhole covers high into the air on columns of water. In Romford, 100 homes were flooded. Around Colchester, heavy hail smashed greenhouses and plastic roof sections and cars were badly pitted. Stones of 1.6 inches (40mm) in diameter fell at Severalls Lane while on the Essex-Suffolk border at Dedham, ice lay six inches deep. Crops were devastated, especially fruit. At Ardleigh, 80 acres of orchards were destroyed with some apples actually split in half.

All clouds have a silver lining and it was reported that powerful Porsches displayed on a garage forecourt near Colchester, which were bombarded by hail, remained unscathed — providing a meteorological boost to their sales potential.

The rain in Chelmsford began with huge drops. All the street lights came on and suddenly torrents of water were falling, as if someone had turned a giant bucket upside down. The thunder sounded like wardrobes being thrown downstairs and marble-sized hail lashed down onto the streets in the great storm of 22nd August, 1987.

It may seem unbelievable after so much rain but, in the summer of 1987, there was a water shortage in parts of Essex. Here, on 12th July, residents of Loughton queue for water from a tanker as thousands of homes were without the vital commodity for the second day running — because of a heatwave. Tanker lorries worked through the night to ferry in supplies to the worst hit areas. A Thames Water spokesman said at the time — "The warm weather made people use far more water and we just couldn't cope".

Too little water, then suddenly too much. In early October it rained and suddenly the rivers could not cope. As the levels grew higher, police polished up on their emergency plan procedures and sandbags were moved into distribution centres. Picture shows the River Colne during the weekend 10th and 11th October. Heavy rain on the Friday and Saturday brought the floods on Sunday. Modern motors had much difficulty but "Master Fred", an 1896 traction engine taking part in a steam rally had no problem. Five days later, with the ground drenched by the persistent rain and trees still in full leaf, came another storm on 16th October, 1987. But that is another story....

Essex hit by a 'hurricane'

16th October, 1987

THURSDAY 15th October, 1987 began innocently. Rivers were rising after long weeks of heavy rain and a brash of wind was teasing the trees that were still in full leaf. At Wallasea in the Crouch Estuary and in the labyrinth of creeks that branch out of the Roach, sailing boats were safely moored in their marinas. At Southend, with seven miles of south-facing foreshore, the promenade joggers and those who enjoy the bracing air, were watching the sea heave in the breeze. At Epping Forest, the footpaths that wind and twist through its 5,500 acres, were soggy and uncomfortable after the recent rain. At Rowhedge on the Colne, a Grade B flood warning was being carefully monitored. A typical windy, damp autumnal day in Essex, with no hint of what was to come.

People went to bed on that Thursday night expecting to rise next morning to familiar sights and sounds, but they were closing their eyes on a world that, in many places, would no longer appear the same again. A storm, destined to be one of the most destructive of the century, was brewing in the English Channel.

All day a moderate but deepening depression had been centering in the Bay of Biscay. The computer in the Met office at Bracknell showed the centre to be south of Cape Finisterre where the pressure stood at 970 millibars. The data and their lack of weatherships made it difficult to ascertain how fast it would deepen and which way it would go. Weathermen knew there would be exceptionally strong winds moving across France, Holland and Belgium. In England, there was no such certainty.

By 10 pm the southern counties of England were feeling the initial blasts of the rising gale with gusts of 46 mph reported inland. Shortly after midnight, the Channel Islands took the full force of the raging storm which was now heading north east towards England. As it did so the wind rose to gusts of more than 100 mph. At 3 am on Friday pressure had plunged to 956 millibars at the centre of the depression which was near Bristol and racing north-eastwards.

The wind roared across the southern landscape. Terrified families woke in fear to discover trees crashing around, or even on, their homes. From the Channel to the Wash the fingers of the hurricane-force winds spread their misery and struck terror into seven million hearts.

Hampshire, Sussex, Surrey and Kent were being lashed by the devastating winds around 4 am. It bulldozed its relentless course into Essex some 60 minutes later leaving a trail of heartbreak and destruction across the county.

At the weather observation station in Shoeburyness, the first gust in excess of 60 knots occurred just before 3 am and, for the next three hours, the wind on this south-facing Essex coastline rarely dropped below that speed. At 4.50, a gust of 87 knots was recorded — exactly 100 mph.

Great swathes of woodland were turned to matchwood. Houses, schools, hotels and even hospitals had chimney pots or roofs lifted and torn away. Electricity pylons fell like skittles, sending high voltage cables writhing and arcing through the night. Lorries toppled over. Greenhouses shattered. Grounded aircraft overturned on several exposed fields.

The Essex Marina, where earlier the boats had been secured for the night, broke its pier foundations and, with its landing stage and craft attached, swept into the mouth of the River Crouch and came to rest on the other side at Burnham.

At Southend, where the joggers and walkers had earlier enjoyed the bracing air, the wind was so powerful that it held back the tide. Boat owners, brave enough to venture outside, found they could walk across the mud as far as the pier head at high tide.

In the mediaeval forest of Epping, the soggy footpaths were quickly obliterated by fallen trees and covered in undergrowth and debris. Trees thumped onto the roads that run by the side of the forest bringing down the cables. Inspecting the damage on the 'morning after' the Forest Conservationists discovered that, compared to the rest of the county, the damage was minimal.

During the next hour, between 5 and 6 am, Essex took a battering. Mrs Sylvia Brown, a postwoman in Canvey Island, was trapped for nearly three hours under a 40-foot poplar in her garden. She died five days later in hospital. Scores of people were trapped in their bedrooms by fallen trees but, miraculously, she was the only fatality in the county.

Trees crashed down everywhere. British Rail's Eastern Region had to clear about 2,000 trees and a Leigh-on-Sea cockle shed from its line before it could resume normal service. The Central line of the

Boats beached at Thorpe Bay.

London Underground that runs above ground between Epping and Ongar was out of action for three days after 60 trees blocked the line.

At Southend, the town took a battering. Boats were hurled out of the water to end up splintered on the seafront or even on the road and scores of beach huts disintegrated to matchwood. Cafes and amusement arcades lost their windows, a 16-pot chimney crashed through the roof of the Railway Hotel, the intensive care unit of Southend Hospital was put out of action when all the windows were smashed and for a time it was necessary to close the operating theatre.

Many roads leading into Romford, Ilford, Harlow and certainly in the heavily wooded areas around Waltham, Ongar, Epping and Chigwell were blocked by fallen trees. Billericay was completely cut off. Dozens of Essex schools suffered too, mostly with roofing problems. St John Payne in Chelmsford lost a complete roof and there was damage to schools in Harwich, Rainham, Romford and Havering. Romford Ice Rink lost a roof as did a block of flats on the Limes Farm Estate at Chigwell.

In Harwich on the River Stour, the *Earl William*, a former Sealink Ferry was safely moored at St George's Quay. The ship had been chartered by the Home Office to serve as a detention ship for immigrants who were waiting for their claims to enter Britain to be heard. Among them were Tamil refugees from war-torn Sri Lanka. In the early hours of the morning, with the wind at its strongest, the vessel broke free from its moorings and rolled into the estuary with nobody in control. It smashed into anchored boats, sinking several, and hit a barge, causing a great hole to appear in the hull of the ship. A tug tried unsuccessfully to hold her but the ship lurched on towards the open sea. A helicopter rescue was considered by the Harbour Board but this was abandoned as the tide slipped and the ship came to rest on sand at Shotley Point, with the terrified refugees wishing they had stayed at home!

In the north of the county, all roads into Saffron Walden were blocked by fallen trees and the police called upon the army to help tackle the chaos. Men from the 9/12th Royal Lancers at Carver Barracks, Wimbish answered the call with axes, saws and recovery vehicles.

In Canvey Island, no fewer than 400 caravans were damaged or destroyed. Small boats at anchor in the east coast estuaries were badly damaged. In Clacton, 100 people had to be moved to bed and breakfast accommodation after their homes were mauled by the wind. Essex firemen received 1,800 calls before breakfast time, compared with a normal total of about 50 for an entire day. Some 700,000 customers of Eastern Electricity were without power. In rural areas water supplies failed and there were very few telephones working in the county.

Many people had lucky escapes. One was old age pensioner, Mrs Marjorie Shipton of Old Harlow who, because of a broken foot, slept in a downstairs room.

A large tree rests against a house in St. John's Avenue, Old Harlow. The occupant, Marjorie Shipton had broken her foot and was sleeping downstairs at the time. She described it as a "lucky break".

During the night a tree fell on the roof just above the bedroom in which she would normally have slept. She described it as a 'lucky break'.

The winds caused great damage in the Dengie Hundred, where 2,000 people called the Essex Fire Brigade for assistance. The sports centre at Burnham lost most of its roof and, at Althorne, one of the oldest buildings in the village, White's Garage was flattened. In Maryland, two workers at Stubbs Engineering works were injured when the roof of their factory was blown off at 7.15 am. At North Fambridge, the Ferry Inn, was badly damaged and a small shed was blown around the garden of the inn, complete with its occupant, Clover the goat.

Such was the magnitude of the storm that almost every person in Essex had a story to tell. The days that followed were not idle ones. Electricity workers had the massive task of re-erecting the huge pylons and re-connecting miles and miles of overhead cables. Eastern Electricity brought in 15 helicopters to survey the lines and to locate faults. More than 250 extra engineers and linesmen were drafted in from other parts of Britain and the army sent men with special lifting gear to various corners of the county to

unravel damaged transformers and cables from the mangled remnants of rain-sodden trees on clogged country lanes. Emergency generators were delivered to hospitals, convalescent homes, meat stores and dairy farms.

For some days parts of the county remained in darkness and developed a new slow life of candlelit meals without television or telephone. Statistics abounded as the final cost was evaluated in millions of pounds. The power of the wind had felled an estimated 15 million trees in the south east and left 19 people dead and hundreds injured. Even before the last road was re-opened, the storm had passed into folklore as one of the most spectacular meteorological events of the century. It was calculated, via the law of averages, that a storm of this magnitude was unlikely to occur again for at least 250 years.

Less than three years later, Essex was reeling again as another great storm hit the county with the most violent fury. This time it occurred in the daytime, left more people dead, caused havoc across the county and made complete mockery of the law of averages!

Unhappy owners attempt tp salvage their craft from the jumble of 60 boats attached to the Essex Wallasea Marina which was swept a mile across the river to Burnham.

In Upminster, the "hurricane" felled trees in a manner that was almost artistic.

Flatford Bridge battered by the wind.

Aerial view of Hadleigh Woods, where thousands of trees were uprooted and great limbs torn from lofty trunks.

One in four of the 2.8 million Eastern Electricity customers lost their power on the night of the storm — a situation never before experienced in the history of the company. 250 extra linesmen and engineers were drafted in to locate and repair the faults, and the army sent in heavy lifting gear to unravel damaged transformers and cables.

Another 'gale of the century'

25th January, 1990

THEY said it was a once-in-a-lifetime storm. Nothing like the October 1987 hurricane could happen again in our lifetime. But just over two years later, a storm almost as severe ripped through Southern England and the Midlands leaving 47 people dead.

The winds were not as strong as they had been in 1987, and fewer trees fell but, occurring in the daytime when everyone was out and about, it caused greater loss of life and widespread disruption which many people will remember forever.

Damage in Essex was extensive on that terrible Burns Day Thursday. The county's Fire and Rescue Service received 2,000 calls and Essex Police answered 244 emergency cases.

The day dawned with severe weather warnings on the radio. The Met Office warned at 6.15 am that some structural damage could occur. As a deep area of low pressure crossed eastwards over central Britain, winds gusted to hurricane force 12 on the southern flank of the depression. At Chelmsford, the gusts reached 86 mph at 2.15 pm and 3 pm. Even in London, one gust reached 87 mph and Stansted Airport recorded its strongest-ever wind speed.

Winds in excess of 80 mph tend to cause damage to homes and this was certainly the case on this occasion — more than 1,500 calls were made to Chelmsford council alone from tenants suffering problems.

The violent winds tore through schools forcing 50 to be closed in Essex the following day. One of the worst hit was St John Payne in Chelmsford which suffered extensive damage to a roof. It was the second blow for the headmaster and his staff, for similar damage occurred in the 1987 storm. Another school, in Harlow, was in such a bad state it was virtually a 'write off'. Essex County Council's clear-up and repair bill ran to £1.2 million and most of that sum was made up from the work needed to make schools safe. Eight in the county were seriously affected.

Some 70,000 homes in southern Essex lost their power as a wall collapsed on to a power supply. Canvey was particularly badly hit. Eastern Electricity flew in 40 skilled linesmen in eight helicopters to restore supplies.

On Canvey Island, a boy of three and his one-year-old sister died in a fire started by a candle used to light their bedroom during a power cut. Their mother, Jacqueline Soper, aged 25, whose first husband choked to death on the night of the October 1987 storm, was seven months pregnant.

Near Broomfield, the A131 was blocked after an electricity cable fell across the road and, in Harlow, emergency services rescued a driver and passengers trapped in their vehicle after a tree fell on it at Greenstead Green. At Nazeing, a fork lift truck driver lost an arm when his vehicle was blown on top of him.

Train services were thrown into chaos and the Fenchurch Street to Barking, Tilbury and Shoeburyness section was closed down. The Braintree line was out of commission and no trains ran on the Wickford - Southminster link. Buses prepared to ferry 100.000 commuters home from London.

Out at sea, conditions were wild. Sealink's UK flagship, St Nicholas was forced to return to Harwich with 150 passengers after having sheltered for 10 hours off the Essex coast.

Aircraft flights were also badly disrupted. Stansted Airport closed during the afternoon. At Southend, a light aircraft was lifted on to the busy railway line and trains were halted.

A lorry, blown over by the gale near Chelmsford, was reported to have been righted again by a later gust. A cabin cruiser was blown high and dry at the Papermill Lock, Little Baddow and a van which somersaulted on the A130 near the Rettendon turnpike finished up on the other side of the carriageway. Seven lorries were blown over near the A12 junction with the A414 and, at South Woodham Ferrers, a passenger was injured when a coach was thrust off the road. Walking, too, was a perilous occupation. Chelmsford High Street was sealed off after a plate glass window was shattered.

There were so many emergencies that ambulance crews decided to suspend their industrial action and help with the crisis. Some 240 calls were made to an emergency control room run by the police at Chelmsford to co-ordinate the activities of 20 army ambulances.

The 13th century St Mary and St Margaret Church, which stood in Stow Maries near Maldon suffered gravely. Strong winds caused the white bell tower to collapse, severely damaging the building. Cressing Temple's 18th century Cart Lodge crumbled, leaving a pile of wood and a dislodged thatched roof.

One bus looks very much like another, except when the wind has hurled it into a ditch

In Maldon, the High Street was closed due to the perils of flying roof tiles and 350 Maldon District Council homes were damaged. At Takeley, there were reports that mink had escaped from a farm.

On the Essex side of London, there was widespread damage. A house collapsed in Chelmsford Road, Walthamstow and scattered scaffolding gave a battleground appearance in Regent Lane, Canning Town.

The Burns Day storm was a prelude to a series of vicious gales which lashed the country during the rest of the winter, and few people will forget the dramatic pictures of the disastrous floods in Towyn, North Wales. In late February, a 200-year-old timber barn at Great Waltham fell like a pack of cards as gales lashed Essex again.

January 1990 was, in spite of the tempestuous winds, a mild month which was a little wetter than normal. The following spring was the driest since 1976.

Nationally, 47 people died as a direct, or indirect, result of the Burns Day storm, compared with 19 in the October 1987 "hurricane", which occurred at night. An estimated four million trees fell, compared with 15 million in 1987. Insurance companies put the national bill at £2,000 million — a similar figure to 1987, but the first event affected a smaller area of England.

Cressing Temple's eighteenth century Cart Lodge, near Braintree after the storm.

Light transport surrenders to the wind at Southend Airport.

CHAPTER 12: 1990 — 1999

1990: This was the warmest year since 1846 with a winter so mild that plants, trees and flowers were some six weeks ahead in growth. However, sharp frosts in April produced the lowest temperature of the 'winter' — the mercury falling to 25F (-4C) in Southend. In July, Britain registered a new high temperature record of 99F (37.2C) at Cheltenham.

1991: The drought continued to make the headlines but, on the 29th, parts of Essex had one of their wettest ever April days when 1.2 inches (30.6mm) fell on Loughton and 1.1 inches (29mm) at Basildon. On 1st August, severe storms broke during the morning. A man was struck by lightning while holding an umbrella at Hartswood Golf Club, Brentwood and was treated for serious burns, while another man suffered a similar fate in a telephone box on Canvey Island. Torrential rain fell. Further flooding occurred on 7th August when Basildon recorded 2.22 inches (56.8mm).

1992: The winter 1991-2 was the driest over much of Essex since 1933-4. At Loughton only 1.75 inches (44.7mm) fell — 27 per cent of the long term average. Compare that with Coniston in the Lake District which registered 29.6 inches (755mm)! On Friday 19th June a small area of low pressure triggered off violent thunderstorms during the afternoon. At Rolphe Primary School, Thorpe-le-Soken, part of the roof of the school was blown into a tree, while other bits were strewn across the High Street.

1993: After the drought during the previous four years and then a dry spring which left the water table 60 feet lower than average in the west of Essex, the weather pendulum swung wildly to the opposite extreme. Places such as Loughton recorded more than 100mm of rain during both September and October. Red flood alerts were issued for the River Roding between Ongar and Loughton and for the Nazeing Brook. Essex firemen attended 178 separate calls. The River Wid surrounded a former mill house as it broke its banks at Widford. At North Weald, cars floated out of showrooms when a waist deep wave of water ripped open homes.

On November 21st, five inches (12 cm) of snow fell between Chelmsford and Billericay.

1994: A sunny dry and warm summer with severe storms in places. During Friday evening June 24th thunderstorms produced strong gusts up to 60 mph with vivid lightning. All over London and into Essex cases of asthma were reported. The likely cause was the stirring up of pollens and pollutants by the airflow in and out of the storms.

November was the warmest recorded over Britain since the 1650s. It was as warm, as May! At the end of the month gardens had the appearance of early summer with many plants in flower.

1995: A frost on May 14th damaged fruit and potatoes at Little Waltham. Overall the summer was fine and dry especially August which was the warmest ever recorded with a mean of 20.5C (69F). Sunshine amounted to more than 270 hours in places.

It was not long before another month, October, was to break records with mean temperatures exceeding 13C (55F). It was also one of the driest with less than 4 mm (0.15 inches) in Colchester. There was a cold December with snow cover on eight days, the most since February 1991.

1996: Unlike many of the winters in the 1990s it was cold and there was some snow. Eight inches fell on the night of February 19th/20th and drifted badly in gale force north east winds. On this night the Thames Barrier was raised for the third time in 24 hours. At Southend, the highest tide since the barrier opened in 1982 was recorded with a height of 3.95 metres (13 feet). Spring was cold and there was frost in May.

The summer was on the warm side again with the hottest weather on June 7th with 32.5C (90.5F) at Leigh on Sea. It almost exceeded the highest temperature ever recorded in Britain for the time of year. There was a wintry end to the year with snow covering the ground near Colchester. Drifting snow was three feet deep at Great Wakering.

1997: A cold start to January. The temperature reached just -3.3C at Galleywood. Two people died at Chelmsford when they fell through a frozen lake while trying to rescue their dog. Drought held centre stage for the rest of the winter. At Colchester it was the driest January with 9.3mm since the weather station opened in 1887. Nationally, the period from April 1995 to December 1996 was the driest sequence since 1767. Rain relieved the drought in June. In fact, it was the wettest on record at Colchester. The summer improved and August was the warmest ever recorded over Essex — higher even than 1995.

1998: Another mild winter and remarkably so on February 13th when the mercury nudged 18C (64F) in Benfleet. Although the county escaped the worst of the Easter floods that swept the Midlands, Colchester still recorded almost 100mm (four inches) for April. On August 1st a deluge flooded the Dartford tunnel and approach roads in Essex. Rainfall exceeded 25 mm in less than an hour. A tornado was seen at Pleshey, Chelmsford, on September 27th.

1999: There was shirtleve weather in early January when Rettendon reached 15C and London had its warmest January for around 155 years. July was dry but severe thunderstorms brought flash floods to Great Maplestead area. After the wettest Essex day ever (*see story page 162*) there were further storms in August which led to the death of a golfer at Chigwell on the 28th. September was the warmest since 1949 and the temperature reached 30C (86F) on the 11th.

The beauty and bleakness of Finchingfield in the snow of February 1991, looking towards the group of cottages which slope down to the frozen village pond. In the background is the great square Norman tower of the church.

The wrong type of snow, 1991

FEBRUARY 1991 brought freezing temperatures and snow — the wrong type of snow, according to British Rail who blamed this powdery variety for clogging up the engines and disrupting services.

Chelmsford Council agreed and described the snowfall as "absolutely abnormal" since the salt they put down failed to thaw it. This was because the temperature was often as low as 18F (-8C) at night and, on one occasion during the day, failed to climb higher than 23F (-5C).

At Admirals Park, two swans became frozen to a river bank and had to be rescued by the RSPCA. One bird was so weak it had to stay in a garage overnight to thaw out.

Essex County Council executive Mark Wilson heard a woman screaming that her dog was trapped between the ice floes on the River Can. He leapt onto the ice — and sank up to his neck in the freezing water. Both he and the beagle dog survived the ordeal. A Chelmsford teenager was not so fortunate. His black mongrel, Sam, ventured onto the ice-covered River Chelmer which gave way under him. Mark waded out, pushing the thick ice aside. He was then forced to swim into deep water and blacked out for a while. Passers-by threw ropes to him and eventually pulled him out. He was taken to hospital, shivering violently, and was wrapped in tin foil. Sam, the dog was also recovered.

A group of flatmates in Springfield Road, Chelmsford, kept warm by digging blocks of snow to build an igloo. Neighbours delivered a card welcoming them to their new home. The snowy spell set in on Wednesday 7th February and lasted for about 10 days. It had been the worst snowfall for four years — since January 1987.

Four years without snow. Now it's time to make up lost time by building the biggest snowman in the world. That was the aim of Roxwell Scouts in February 1991, who wanted a place in the Guinness Book of Records with their 22 foot 3 inch giant snowman which towered above a field in Writtle.

Four dry years and a water crisis

The great drought continued

CRACKED river beds, dried-up reservoirs, vanishing wildlife, hosepipe restrictions, exasperated fishing enthusiasts, garden centres that advertised water butts instead of sprinklers. In our once green and pleasant, but then arid, land the summer months had become synonymous with water regulations. Following four dry years and two decades of low rainfall, the drought was officially the worst of the century and scientists warned that Eastern England might become an ecological dustbowl.

The situation may not have been as serious as in California where gardeners were dyeing their lawns green, but nonetheless, rainfall amounts showed an annual deficit for four successive years — a shortfall not experienced since the eighteenth century. It was all because of global warming, went the popular theory, but this received short shrift from the Met Office who said that global warming had not been proved and the drought was due entirely to the general variability of the British climate.

A measure of how extreme the weather had become can be highlighted by measurements from Hanningfield Reservoir. By June 1992, the rainfall deficit was approaching 14 inches (358mm) which was more than 1,400 tons per acre. In parts of the South East, the deficit was close to 20 inches.

The year 1988 started the trend with rainfall around 92 per cent of average but it was in 1989 that the word 'drought' really began to hit the headlines. Shoeburyness measured just 0.02 inches (0.7mm) during May, its driest since records began there in 1921. Temperatures, even on the coast at Leigh-on-Sea, reached 83F (28C) on the 24th and Clacton recorded a sunshine total higher than any month since July 1911. Over all the year received just 86 per cent of the annual average fall.

A reprieve caused by the mild but wet winter was not to last, for the torrid conditions of the 1990 summer caused reservoir levels to subside and dire warnings about global warming were given their first airing. Essex was often shrouded in smoke from heath, field and woodland fires, while high-factor sun-tan oil became a necessity for many. Dust devils, usually more at home in the Sahara, whirled over a parched landscape. At Great Baddow it was straw that rained down as spinning hot air picked up the contents of nearby fields.

High pressure held sway throughout most of July so that at Colchester only 1955 and 1935 were drier. Harlow recorded 86F (30C) and Essex Fire Service was answering 100 calls a day.

The heat intensified further in early August. Chelmsford's Riverside Pool received nearly 3,000 visitors a day and the temperatures rose to the mid-nineties Fahrenheit. Conditions became hazardous in the countryside. Firemen called to a grass fire at Cressing suddenly found their appliance on fire as the capricious wind changed direction. It was badly damaged but the crew escaped unhurt. At another blaze at Stondon Massey, a school stood in the path of the flames. It took firemen from 11 stations from Ongar to Chelmsford to control the situation.

An almost forgotten hazard manifested itself at Upminster. As part of the Open Day entertainments at the railway station, the last underground steam locomotive, 92-year-old Number One Metropolitan was to make six trips to Upney. However, during its journey it became a 'chariot of fire' as sparks from the 'fire box' set off a string of line-side fires which burnt down 30 garden sheds and 60 acres of railway embankment. After 53 calls from the public to the emergency services, the engine was swiftly replaced.

The stifling conditions led to the demise of a life-sized waxwork Norman knight at Stansted's Mountfitchet Castle. It melted. All that was left, said a sad owner Alan Goldsmith, was a pool of wax, two glass eyes and a helmet.

Essex Water imposed a ban on hoses and sprinklers as Hanningfield Reservoir dropped to its lowest-ever level, exposing a 50-yard stretch of cracked clay around the periphery. The National Rivers Authority banned more than 200 Essex farmers from using the Chelmer and Blackwater for irrigation purposes and employed aerial surveillance to impose the order. Some water was transferred from the Great Ouse Groundwater Scheme to augment supplies.

A year later the same concern was voiced by the water companies. Hanningfield was just 67 per cent full in September 1991 and Abberton, near Colchester, was 62 per cent. More typical values would be around 80 per cent, the difference representing about 800 million lost gallons of water.

In west Essex around Ongar, a two year hosepipe ban was extended into its third year as winter rains failed. A vast area of high pressure settled over Britain producing the driest winter since 1933-4. Loughton measured only 27 per cent of the long-term average rainfall. Very little rain managed to soak its way through the Chiltern Hills to replenish natural aquifers that supply this area with 75 per

The Essex Water Superintendent, Mike Pointing on the dry shoreline of Hanningfield Reservoir during the first week of August 1990, when the temperatures exceeded 93F (34C).

cent of its tap water.

The seriousness of the situation was summed up by a Three Valleys Water Company official who said the worst drought in living memory was outside any predictions, or the most dire estimates, that the company had in their strategic planning. They were heading into unchartered territory.

As the drought tightened its grip during the spring of 1992, the Ministry of Agriculture introduced an amber and red alert system for East Anglian farmers which gave advanced warnings of the inevitable widespread restrictions. May, with almost 50 per cent above the average sunshine and warmer than any of its predecessors since 1833, did not help matters.

Rain in July was followed by a three-day downpour in August which gave as much rain as the whole of the previous winter. This was most welcome but above average rainfall for several successive years was what was really needed to properly replenish reservoirs and rivers.

Giant hailstones kill migrating birds

September 18th, 1992

AN ornithological tragedy struck south-east Essex when thousands of migrating birds on Foulness island were killed by hailstones — some more than two inches in diameter.

The culprit was a spectacular electric storm caused by low pressure moving into the county from the south west. For more than four hours lightning lit up the sky and thunder crashed. Hundreds of homes were plunged into darkness, numerous burglar alarms were activated and, once again, rescue teams were stretched to the limit.

As Shoeburyness Met Office recorded 20mm of rain and a single wind gust of 35 knots a spokesman said: "It looked more dramatic than it actually was because the storm remained directly overhead for so long".

Even so, the storm left a long trail of damage and injury. A security guard at Basildon was struck by lightning. He survived. Two high voltage supply stations in Wickford were hit, cutting power in more than 1,000 homes. Police in Rayleigh and Southend were plagued by false alarms as the storm played havoc with their security systems.

At Terling a family of four were made homeless when their house was seriously damaged by lightning. Pauline and Derek Wager told how, luckily, they left their bedroom just minutes before the roof exploded. Within moments the upstairs of their home in Gambles Green, Terling, was engulfed in flames.

In the Brentwood and Colchester areas police received more than 500 emergency calls and fire crews were summoned to Brentwood's Post House Hotel to pump out floodwater.

October 20th: More electric storms, more damage to homes and more remarkable escapes from injury. At Ingatestone volunteer firemen saved a bungalow struck by lightning. The owner John Murphy and his son Paul escaped from their blazing home.

At Chelmsford a young girl was left dazed but unharmed when the street outside Moulsham School was illuminated by sheet lightning. It was believed that Sarah-Jane Fagg's Doc Marten shoes saved her from serious harm.

Roofless. Derek and Pauline Wager in the devastated bedroom of their home at Gambles Green, Terling.

November 5th: Nineteen Danbury scouts needed first aid when a heavy wind blew their Guy Fawkes bonfire out of control. The Marconi St John Ambulance set up a makeshift treatment couch in front of their vehicle and took many to hospital.

In the heat of summer. Firefighters at Little Waltham where 100 acres of standing corn were destroyed.

Meet the overheated motorist

July/August 1995

ANOTHER memorable summer. Sunny and warm in July and exhaustingly hot in August — the hottest August, in fact, of the century — a month of barbecues, blazes, cloudless skies and a new phenomenon. The overheated motorist.

Road rage reared its ugly head for the first time in August 1995 and quickly became an epidemic that refused to go away. As tempers across Essex became more and more frayed a set of guidelines was issued by the clergy to help defuse the situation. "Don't worry about the weather", they advised. "Lock the doors and windows, stay in your cars and avoid eye contact when confronted by a hot-headed thug!"

Trouble on the road and trouble at sea. The RNLI reported one of its busiest ever months in Essex with double the usual number of calls. "People drive to the coast from London", said a spokesman, "and they're hot. So they sit on their inflatables, get blown out to sea and we have to rescue them".

Little wonder that families headed for the sea. On the first day of August, Southend was hotter than Malaga or Barcelona. In many parts of Essex the roads melted and buckled under the heat. Great tailbacks built up on the A12. The excess heat and lack of rain was a reminder once more that global warming was more a certainty than a theory.

Things had first begun to heat up in the second half of June. On the 30th the mercury climbed to 86F (30C) in Writtle. The month was dry, with only 40 per cent of the normal June rainfall and the last 13 days of the month were rainless.

July was warm and sunny throughout culminating in a high of 88F (31C) on the 31st. The average maximum temperature for the month was 77F (25.3C) — just below the record level set in July 1983.

As the temperatures soared into the nineties in early August, Essex firefighters were at full stretch. In just five days they were called to 191 grass and countryside fires. Some incidents required eight to 10 appliances. "The fire fighting operations are sapping our strength", said a spokesman.

One hundred acres of standing corn was destroyed at Little Waltham and it took 60 firemen to tackle the inferno. There were more big fires at Ingatestone and Great Totham when families were evacuated from their homes.

In north-west Essex helicopters were used to track the course of a fire and the A120 was closed over a five-mile stretch.

There were problems at Colchester General Hospital where the ventilation system virtually broke down in the blistering heat. Health chiefs sought guidance. There were problems, too, in Harlow where a fight developed outside a night club on the hottest night of the year. Four men were injured.

Tourists who eventually beat the traffic jams and escaped the worst of the road rage to reach the sea found fresh problems. Heat exhaustion, too much sun, harmful rays and — a plague of wasps.

Yes, the summer of '95 had a real sting in its tail and nowhere was worse than the south west of the county. For almost a month the environmental division of Epping Forest Council fielded an average of 37 calls a day. More than 90 people were badly stung. Oh, come winter with thine cooling howl!

Holidaymakers, fruit farmers, wine growers and sunworshippers who desperately wanted a return of the famously hot summers of 1989 and 1990 had their prayers answered in the most glorious way. As temperatures soared into the nineties in July 1994 — with a high of 32.3C at Leigh-on-Sea — weathermen announced that it was the third warmest July of the century. But would there be another? The answer was 'yes'. July 1995 shared third place with 1994 and 1911 in the century's tables, behind the Julys of 1983 and 1976. August also saw record-breaking temperatures, October was one of the warmest ever known and November was the driest since 1956. The photograph shows the crowds below the helter skelter at Southend beach on the last day of July 1995. It really was hot stuff.

The flashiest county in Britain — and that's official

January 1996: Nine snowless Januarys in Essex. Teenagers trying to remember when they last used a toboggan. Pensioners grateful that the winters were no longer like "the ones they used to know!"

Would it last? The answer was 'no'. Six inches of the white stuff fell in Essex on January 29th and brought places such as Southend to a standstill.

As temperatures plunged, panic set in across the county. Asda at Shoebury ran out of bread. Milk and sugar disappeared from the shelves the following day. Taxis were in short supply, Marks and Spencer sent their staff home early.

The National Grid had the answer. "People seem to think this is a crisis", said a spokesman. "We have enough generating capacity to meet this lot. Stop panicking!"

June 1996: Essex certainly pays the penalty for being the driest and one of the flattest counties in England. As a new series of electric storms hit the county Eastern Electricity Board admitted that Rayleigh, Canvey, Billericay and Great Wakering attract more lightning strikes than any other part of the country.

"Essex is our worst area in this respect", a spokesman said. "It tends to be flatter, hotter and more humid. The high pylons are vulnerable. On one day we dealt with 260 faults compared to a daily average elsewhere of nine".

As the company announced that the electrical equipment was being updated and storm tracking gear installed, the head of emergency services, Mr Bill Slegg, explained that electricity within the thunder cloud discharges to earth and sets up a surge along power lines.

Monsoon Monday breaks county record

July 5th, 1999

A DAY that the residents of Stansted, Braintree and especially the Hedinghams will never forget. Two violent thunderstorms each unleashed a deluge of tropical proportions. So hard did it rain that traffic came to a standstill, queues built up for many miles around, drains failed to cope and swirling brown floodwater invaded scores of homes.

Monsoon Monday, as it was called, produced 122mm (4.56inches) of rain at Sible Hedingham and if this is officially recognised it will go down in history as the heaviest daily fall ever measured in the county. It was followed by a massive mop-up operation as victims tried to salvage what was left in their homes. *(see front cover photograph)*

Residents of St James Street in Castle Hedingham described it as the "worst flooding in living memory". Local councillor, David Breedon of Sible Hedingham said: "I've heard stories about flooding in the 1970s but there was nothing like today. I hope we shall never see anything like this again."

As engineers restored phone lines and electricity supplies, earth removers were clearing tonnes of soil and clay after a bank had collapsed under the weight of the rainwater, trapping a pregnant mum-to-be in her home at Wethersfield Road, Sible Hedingham.

The woman was not hurt but emergency vehicles including a paramedic with fire brigade escort, struggled to reach her.

In Swan Street thousands of gallons of water spilled out after flood gates on a brook were opened. Firemen had to pump out 400 gallons a minutes outside the Sugar Loaf pub

It was the same story in Stansted. At the height of the storm a "river" several feet deep flowed into Lower Street and sent a tidal wave into nearby premises. At Great Maplestead 73 mm fell in two hours with flood water a metre deep.

There was severe flooding right across the Upper Colne Valley. By contrast, in Colchester, only 9mm of rain fell during the entire month of July.

Welcome to the new damp, very damp millennium

2000: The new millennium continued the trend to mild winters which had been established for much of the 1990s and it proved to be the sunniest on record. However, April and July were chilly and wet. In fact, April was the wettest on record for many weather stations in the county with some places exceeding 100mm (four inches).

In May, there was dramatic flooding on the A130 at Benfleet and the A127 at Rayleigh on the 27th when 50mm (two inches) of rain fell. Over the south and east of Britain there were 92 flood warnings.

On July 9th parts of Essex, including Southend, had more than 26mm (one inch) of rain. Laindon was badly flooded to a depth of several feet with 500 yards of road impassable. This was the forerunner to the "millennium floods" of late October/November which brought misery to almost every river valley in Britain.

Why Essex is in such a whirl

1996-2000: The news in 1996 that Essex topped the premier division of lightning strikes was followed three years later by an even more dramatic revelation. "You are in the heart of twister country", said a local newspaper.

It was true. Figures released by the Tornado and Storm Research Organisation (Torro) showed that the county received above-average incidences of tornadoes and water spouts. Of the 42 reported tornadoes across the country in 1998, five of them occurred in Essex.

A tornado is a violently rotating column of air which is usually associated with a thunderstorm although as many as a third occur without the big thunder claps. The air rotates in a helix but in the centre of a tornado, winds are actually very light and descend towards the ground. They typically last a few minutes tracking across land for about three miles and have a diameter of 20 to 100 yards.

Wind speeds are usually below 113mph but at the more extreme end some track for over 100 kilometres and have winds approaching 300mph. Such tornadoes are rare anywhere in the world.

In April 1998 the people of Colchester saw an embryonic tornado form over the town. It hovered politely over the shopping centre for a few minutes but to the disappointment of stunned shoppers never touched ground to become the "real thing".

A week later Adrian Rushton, Colchester Gazette photographer captured a similar funnel cloud formation over the Stour Valley. Once again it passed away

This is twister country and here is the Stour Valley funnel cloud taken by Adrian Rushton.

harmlessly.

Not so in 1999. In April a tea-time twister brought chaos to the little village of Pentlow, near Sudbury. With winds at about 100mph it brought down power lines, smashed every pane of glass in a greenhouse, tore down a 30 foot length of fencing, ripped tiles off a roof, overturned a heavy fountain and destroyed a garage.

Pamela Bowers was alone with her dog in her remote bungalow as the drama unfolded. She watched in horror as her pet's

kennel was picked up three feet by the twister and hurled 20 feet across the garden. The wooden structure went spinning round the garden with the yelping dog inside. "The twister came from nowhere", she said. "I felt I was in the middle of an American disaster movie. I could not believe what I was seeing."

The Pentlow tornado struck only a mile from where, in 1947, a similar twister brought down the spire of St Peter and St Paul's church, at Foxearth.

Towns marooned as millennium floods strike with a vengeance

October/November 2000

UNTIL Sunday October 29 the great floods of 2000 had been confined to the Medway flood plain in Kent and the towns of Lewes, Uckfield, Selsey and Bognor in Sussex. Now Essex, along with other English counties, was to experience the power of the wind and the force of the water pouring into town centres and across farmland as a furious gale swept across the county.

All day Sunday the rain and the wind were unrelenting. As the wind reached speeds of 97 mph in parts of southern England fallen trees severed power supplies and blocked roads while scores of properties were damaged. By Monday morning, two inches of rain had fallen and police across Essex had taken more than 1,000 flood-related calls — 500 of which were 999 calls.

Emergency units from across the county were called in, including members of the Marine Service and the underground search unit. Essex Fire and Rescue Service fielded an additional 381 emergency calls.

Two of the most dramatic rescues were those of an eight-months pregnant woman who was stranded in her flooded home at Waltham Abbey and a 92-year-old with heart problems, trapped in Nazeing.

By Monday morning one month's rainfall had fallen in 24 hours and there were warnings of another low pressure building up in the Atlantic. The railways, already crippled by speed restrictions imposed after the crash at Hatfield earlier in the month, were almost at a standstill.

In Halstead, and villages throughout the Colne Valley, the river overtopped its defences leaving the town's business centre knee deep in water and causing thousands of pounds worth of damage.

At Ongar, stranded drivers were forced to seek refuge in a restaurant alongside the A414 for up to 11 hours as flood waters surged across the road. At Loughton, the High Road was under two feet of murky brown floodwater which lapped into shops. At Woodford Bridge, hundreds of residents had to be evacuated from their homes in Chigwell Road and Manor Road as the River Roding burst its banks. An evacuation centre was set up by Redbridge Council. At Chingford, the normally tranquil River Ching was transformed into a wild flood that appeared so rapidly that home owners struggled desperately to move their belongings upstairs.

Waltham Abbey suffered more than most. Residents of the notorious flood-prone Broomstick Road said they were given no warning and when Cobbins Brook was eventually placed on "severe flood alert" status a river was already pouring through their doors. The Environment Agency disagreed. Spokesman Sarah Wallace said: "During our Flood Awareness Week in September we sent letters to everyone on flood risk offering to call them if a flood warning was issued. We had few replies".

Shops and banks across the country were forced to close and others were manned by a skeleton staff because of the huge travel disruption. London was among the worst-hit areas. It was estimated that 10 per cent of the capital's workforce were unable to get to their office. According to the London Chamber of Trade it cost up to £100 million in lost production. Hundreds of roads were blocked and motorists spent several hours trying to reach their destinations.

As Michael Meacher, the environment minister admitted for the first time that global warming was almost certainly a "contributory cause" of the extreme weather conditions, Met Office forecasters said the conditions were created by a depression coming in off the Atlantic and these were fairly regular occurences. This latest one just happened to be more severe.

As the drama continued to unfold safety campaigners throughout the country said there would have been fewer accidents if the clocks had not gone back one hour to Greenwich Mean Time on Saturday night. "Every year as soon as the clocks go back we start to see an increase in accidents", said a RoSPA safety adviser. This was certainly the case on Sunday".

Although Essex escaped the extent of misery which had affected North Yorkshire and the towns and villages along the Severn valley there were plenty of communities on flood alert and a vast distribution of sandbags was carried out across the county.

After almost a week of continuous heavy rain the skies cleared, the floods subsided and the beleaguered people of Essex continued with the heartbreaking job of mopping up and contacting insurance companies. On Monday November 6, after another day of torrential rain, the floods returned with a vengeance.

This time home owners in the Colne Valley suffered again. At Great Yeldham the main road was under

(continued on page 162)

(continued from previous page)

three feet of water and the village completely cut off as the river broke its banks. The residents of Sible Hedingham, now veterans of such wretchedness, watched in vain as firefighters battled to save properties in Castle Street. Sub-officer Peter Robertson said: "There is nowhere to drain off the water. It is returning as fast as we pump it out".

White Colne suffered repeat flooding. So did Chappel, Bulmer, Greenstead Green and Gosfield.

Controversy was not far away. Angry residents were incensed by Braintree Council's decision to *sell* sandbags to desperate home owners. The council responded by saying they had distributed 1,200 and had a further 3,000 people waiting for them. There simply weren't enough to go around.

By Monday night the Environment Agency had introduced 52 severe flood alerts across 33 rivers and then said that the worst was still to come. Britain was in the grip of one of the most widespread weather events.

Right across England but, especially Essex and the South-East, tiny streams, becks, burns, courses and creeks were bursting their confines to reveal their ancient powers. Long-forgotten springs in low-lying areas, miles away from rivers, were bursting into life. Some were under roads and housing estates, proving the folly yet again of Government plans to build thousands of new homes on flood plains.

High water mark: Loughton High Road on Monday October 30th.

Sixteen months ago a mother-to-be from Sible Hedingham was trapped by a mud slide. Now there was an even greater emergency in the village as two midwives dramatically hitched a ride with 999 crews to reach Allison Hardwick. Allison, who had gone into labour a week early,on Monday November 6th, had been told by doctors to have the baby in hospital. The village was entirely cut off but Sally Watkins (in a fire engine) and Edwina Chaplin (in a police Range Rover) made it through the floods to the family home where Allison was waiting. Picture shows the proud parents, Allison and John with baby Jamie who was delivered just in time.

Under the weather: This is Monday morning October 30th in Broomstick Hall Road, Waltham Abbey.

Retriever: A firefighter saves a family and two dogs as the waters rise in Chigwell Road, Woodford Bridge.

Unlucky: Somewhere below the murky flood waters lies Stondon Road, Ongar. In publishing this picture
The Guardian *reminded its readers that the flooding occurred exactly 13 years and 13 days after the
Great Storm of 1987.*

Two canoeists make the most of conditions as Chigwell Road at Charlie Brown's roundabout is flooded.

Essex highs and lows

HOTTEST DAY
97F (36C) on
19th August, 1932
at Halstead

COLDEST NIGHT
-5F (-21C) on
7th February, 1879
at Aveley End

WETTEST DAYS
4.56 inches (115.8mm)
on 1st August, 1888
at Romford and
3.90 inches (99mm)
in less than two hours
on 26th July, 1941
at Writtle.

DRIEST YEAR
Southminster with
9.94 inches (254mm)
in 1921.

**DRIEST PLACE
IN THE U.K.**
St Osyth
with an average of
20.2 inches (513 mm)
of rain annually.

STRONGEST WIND
101mph at
Shoeburyness
on 16th October, 1987

SUNNIEST YEAR
Many places such as
Rettendon enjoyed
between 1,800 - 1,900
hours of sun in 1990.

COLDEST WINTER
The winter of 1962-3
was the coldest
in Essex since 1740.

Stand by with those sandbags: flooding is now a way of life

INTO the new millennium and the weather in Essex is settling into a familiar pattern with warmer winters, more violent storms and an increased risk of flooding. Perversely, it remains the driest county in the British Isles.

The winter of 1999 was typical of what everyone has come to expect. On New Year's Day a record 5,000 people flocked to the Peter Pan playground on Southend's seafront. A warm January with a high of 15C at Rettendon was followed by warmer than average readings for the months that followed, including April.

Andy Yateman from the London Weather Service said at the time: "The air is coming from the south-west and over the Atlantic. We have got higher temperatures than we should have at this time of the year. The general trend is that winters are getting warmer but it is difficult to link this with global warming at the moment".

It was the same story in January 2000 - very mild and snowless and, by the end of February, Essex was on course to its sunniest winter on record.

The heavy rain followed. The wettest April on record. Thunderstorms in May, with the Bank Holiday a complete washout and dramatic flooding at Rochford, Benfleet and Rayleigh. Unusually severe summer rain in June. More floods in July and then the great "millennium" floods of October/November 2000 which brought misery to much of the country.

There is no doubt that climate change has made Essex, with its many rivers, inlets, creeks and valleys a "hot-spot" for flooding in which the risk to lives and property could possibly increase tenfold over the next century.

The Environment Agency says that while the North and West will see the greatest increase in rainfall, the danger of flooding is greatest in the South-East where most of the new development is likely to take place.

In Essex, those sudden intense thunderstorms are likely to continue and there will be a danger of flooding of low-lying land due to the rise in sea level.

This century, the sea is expected to rise by 15-50cm as glaciers and snowfields melt. By the 2050s, the rise in level due to climate change will increase the frequency of dangerously high tides from once a century to once a decade. Essex again is under threat.

Essex beware. Left to right Bob Ogley, Mark Davison and Ian Currie, authors of the Essex Weather Book, at a typically blustery Hanningfield Reservoir in 1992. The real danger though will come from the sea.

INDEX

The Authors

BOB OGLEY

Bob was born in Sevenoaks, has lived all his life in the county and is proud to be a Kentish Man. An author of more than a dozen books he has travelled extensively in pursuit of information and has discovered an unexpected supplementary career as a speaker to organisations. He is also a regular broadcaster on BBC Radio Kent.

Bob is a former editor of *The Sevenoaks Chronicle* and author of *In The Wake of The Hurricane* — the book on the great storm of 1987 which went into the top ten bestseller lists and stayed there for seven successive months. He has also written *Kent at War, Biggin on The Bump* and *Doodlebugs and Rockets*. His latest is a history on Kent in the 20th century which comes in four volumes. The books he has published have raised more than £95,000 for various charities.

MARK DAVISON

Mark has always shown a keen interest in the weather. As a child he could not be persuaded to come indoors out of the snow. When, as a teenager, the great storm hit Hook in 1973 he was reprimanded by his parents for going off in search of news stories rather than helping them mop up their flooded home.

After leaving school in Kingston, he joined the Kingston Borough News just in time to cover the 1976 drought stories. Later he joined the Surrey Mirror Series and is now community editor at Reigate, the town where he lives.

For a number of years he has compiled a local history page in his newspaper which is still a popular feature today.

Mark has written several local history books. The most recent is *Tolworth Remembered.*

IAN CURRIE

Ian has always been fascinated by the ever changing moods and patterns of our skies.

The spectacular thunderstorm of September 1958 and the prolonged deep winter snows of 1962-63 were childhood memories that have never faded.

Sharing his interest with others has been a feature of Ian's life. He writes a weekly weather column for a number of Surrey newspapers and is now a full-time freelance weatherman, author and speaker. Ian is also Telewest's Channel 17 TV Weatherman.

A graduate of Geography and Earth Science, he regularly talks to local groups and societies.

He is a Member of the Climatological Observers Link and is a Fellow of the Royal Meteorological Society, and publishes a quarterly magazine *Weather Eye.*

FROGLETS FAMILY — Telephone 01959 562972: Fax 01959 565365

COUNTY WEATHER SERIES
By Bob Ogley, Ian Currie and Mark Davison

The Kent Weather Book
ISBN 1 872337 90 2..........................£10.99

The Sussex Weather Book
ISBN 1 872337 13 9..........................£10.99

The Norfolk and Suffolk Weather Book
Paperback ISBN 1 872337 99 6............£9.95
Hardback ISBN 1 872337 98 8..........£16.95

The Hampshire and Isle of Wight
Weather Book
ISBN 1 872337 20 1.............................£9.95

The Berkshire Weather Book
ISBN 1 872337 48 1.............................£9.95

HURRICANE SERIES

In The Wake of The Hurricane
National Edition paperback by Bob Ogley
ISBN 0 9513019 1 8 (Temp o.p)..........£8.95

Surrey In The Hurricane
by Mark Davison and Ian Currie
ISBN 0 9513019 2 6.............................£8.95

Eye on The Hurricane (Eastern Counties)
Paperback ISBN 0 9513019 6 9............£7.95
Hardback ISBN 0 9513019 7 7..........£11.95

WAR AND AVIATION SERIES

Biggin On The Bump
(the most famous fighter station in the world
by Bob Ogley
Paperback ISBN 1 872337 05 8...........£9.99
Hardback ISBN 1 872337 10 4.........£16.99

Doodlebugs and Rockets by Bob Ogley
Paperback ISBN 1 872337 21 X.........£10.99

Kent at War (1939-1945) by Bob Ogley
Paperback ISBN 1 872337 82 1..........£10.99
Hardback ISBN 1 872337 49 X.........£16.99

Surrey at War (1939-1945)
Paperback ISBN 1 872337 65 1...Temp o.p.
Hardback ISBN 1 872337 70 8.........£14.95

Westerham and
Crockham Hill in the War by Helen Long
ISBN 1 872337 40 6.............................£8.95

OTHER LOCAL HISTORY BOOKS

Underriver: Samuel Palmer's Golden Valley
By Griselda Barton and Michael Tong
ISBN 1 872337 45 7.............................£9.95

Tales of Old Tonbridge
by Frank Chapman
ISBN 1 872337 55.4.............................£8.95

email: frogletspublications @bobogley.co.uk

Tales of Old Tunbridge Wells
by Frank Chapman
ISBN 1 872337 25 2..........................£14.95

Sevenoaks Chronicle of the Century
by Bob Ogley and Roger Perkins
ISBN 1 872337 26 0..........................£14.95

CHRONICLE SERIES

Kent Chronicle of the 20th Century
by Bob Ogley

Volume One
ISBN Hardback 1 872337 24 4..........£16.99
ISBN Paperback 1 872337 19 8.........£10.99

Volume Two
ISBN Hardback 1 872337 84 8..........£16.99
ISBN Paperback 1 872337 89 9.........£10.99

Volume Three
ISBN Hardback 1 872337 16 3..........£16.99
ISBN Paperback 1 872337 11 2.........£10.99

Volume Four
ISBN Hardback 1 872337 06 6..........£16.99
ISBN Paperback 1 872337 01 5.........£10.99

Boxed set Hardback 1872337 15 5....£65.00
Boxed set Paperback 1872337 75 9....£45.00